A Track to the Water's Edge

Books by Howard Thurman

THE NEGRO SPIRITUAL SPEAKS OF LIFE AND DEATH

JESUS AND THE DISINHERITED

DEEP IS THE HUNGER

MEDITATIONS OF THE HEART

THE CREATIVE ENCOUNTER

DEEP RIVER

THE GROWING EDGE

FOOTPRINTS OF A DREAM

THE INWARD JOURNEY

TEMPTATIONS OF JESUS

DISCIPLINES OF THE SPIRIT

THE LUMINOUS DARKNESS

THE CENTERING MOMENT

THE SEARCH FOR COMMON GROUND

A TRACK TO THE WATER'S EDGE

A Track
to the Water's Edge

The Olive Schreiner Reader

Edited by
HOWARD THURMAN

HARPER & ROW, PUBLISHERS
New York · Evanston · San Francisco · London

Acknowledgment is made to Syfrets Trust and Executor Company, Grahams-town, South Africa, for permission to reprint selections from *Stories, Dreams and Allegories* and *From Man to Man.*

FIRST EDITION

STANDARD BOOK NUMBER: 06-068076-8

LIBRARY OF CONGRESS CATALOG CARD NUMBER: 72-78068

Designed by C. Linda Dingler

"For what do I go to this far land which no one has ever reached? *Oh, I am alone! I am utterly alone!*"

And Reason, that old man, said to her, "Silence! what do you hear?"

And she listened intently, and she said, "I hear a sound of feet, a thousand times ten thousand and thousands of thousands, and they beat this way!"

He said, "They are the feet of those that shall follow you. Lead on! make a track to the water's edge! Where you stand now, the ground will be beaten flat by ten thousand times ten thousand feet." And he said, "Have you seen the locusts how they cross a stream? First one comes down to the water-edge, and it is swept away, and then another comes and then another, and then another, and at last with their bodies piled up a bridge is built and the rest pass over."

She said, "And, of those that come first, some are swept away, and are heard of no more; their bodies do not even build the bridge?"

"And are swept away, and are heard of no more—and what of that?" he said.

"And what of that—" she said.

"They make a track to the water's edge."

"They make a track to the water's edge—." And she said, "Over that bridge which shall be built with our bodies, who will pass?"

He said, *"The entire human race."*

And the woman grasped her staff.

And I saw her turn down that dark path to the river.

Olive Schreiner, *Dreams*

Contents

Contents

Acknowledgments

It is in order that I express appreciation to the following:

Alice Ratner, my secretary, for her critical eye, her patience, and her resourcefulness;

Virginia Maw, Assistant Professor of Librarianship, Sacramento State University, for bringing to my attention and securing books and other material with which I was not acquainted;

May Mary Tekse, for finding a copy of *Thoughts on South Africa* for which I had searched many years;

Virginia Scardigli, teacher of English in the Palo Alto School System, for making available her notes from research done at the University of California;

Anne Korn, artist, for the line drawings of early Bushman cave paintings;

Sue Bailey Thurman, my wife, whose constant encouragement surrounded the entire undertaking;

George L. Collins, who first introduced me to the writings of Olive Schreiner.

Howard Thurman

Introduction
By Howard Thurman

The year was 1925. The place, Pawling, New York. The setting, an informal conference of some twenty-five students and other young adults. We had come together in a resort hotel, closed for the summer, to spend ten days in discussion and reading aloud. One evening when we were gathered around the huge fireplace in the common room of the hotel I had my first encounter with the writings of Olive Schreiner. The experience lives fully in my recall—even the smell of the burning logs, the faces reflected in the glow of the fire, the voice of Shorty Collins reading from a book called *Dreams,* by Olive Schreiner. I had never heard of her, nor had I ever read anything like "The Hunter," the particular dream to which I was listening.

It seemed that all my life long I was being readied for such an encounter. Through the years since that particular time, I have secured all available works of this gifted woman. Her ideas have influenced my own thought at a very profound level. When I discovered that she was South African, I became immediately suspicious and felt guilty that I was so affected by her. My initial investigation in an effort to find who she was and "how come" was urgent. I had to answer the critical question, How could a white woman born and reared in South Africa think as she thought and feel about man as she felt? But I could not know what she thought unless my reading took me beyond the collection of her dreams and allegories. My own temperament was most congenial to her allegories and prose poems called *Dreams*. As literary art forms they made music I was attuned to hear. But I had to know more.

Systematically, I sought and found all of her works available in the United States in the late twenties and early thirties: *The Story of An African Farm; Undine; From Man to Man; Dreams; Dreams, Stories and Allegories; Trooper Peter Halket of Mashonaland; Dream Life and Real Life; Woman and Labor;* and "The Dawn of Civilization," a rather extensive article that appeared in *The London Nation and Athenaeum* in 1921. Then I secured the two volumes edited by her husband, Cronwright-Schreiner: *Life of Olive Schreiner* and *The Letters of Olive Schreiner.* Only recently was I able to acquire *Thoughts on South Africa; Closer Union, a Letter by Olive Schreiner; A Letter on the Jew.*

I begin, then, with the simple query, who was Olive Schreiner? She was an Englishwoman born in South Africa of missionary parents. But that says little. What kind of man and woman gave birth to this child who was in time to become one of the most famous writers South Africa has yet produced? In Vera Buchanan-Gould's *Not Without Honour, the Life and Writings of Olive Schreiner,* the opening paragraph gives a sensitive, insightful answer.

The scene is set in London. The year, 1836. . . . Napoleon has been dead 15 years, the revolutions of 1830 are hardly forgotten, and across the Channel Metternich waits in Lombardy to pounce eagle-like on any disturbance of the peace. The Industrial Revolution is changing the face of rural England and giving a new direction to European politics. Business rivalry is beginning to fester among the peoples of the West, and imperialism is soon to become the gospel of England. But at that moment, Great Britain is being swept by a wave of popular enthusiasm for the Wesleyan Movement and the Evangelical Revival, similar to that which is sweeping Germany for the Lutheran Revival. The London Missionary Society . . . has begun to send numbers of men to the Cape and its barbaric hinterland. A body of young people are decorously gathered together at a revival meeting. The young gentlemen are, for the most part, theological students at Islington College who are preparing to go out to the four corners of the earth in the service of the Church Missionary Society, and the dainty young ladies . . . are the daughters of middle-class English families to whom the conversion of the heathen is a matter of vast concern. . . . "Who will go and join the throng?" the young people sang fervently, and as the words of the hymns changed to "I will go and join the throng," a certain Miss Rebecca Lyndall, a daughter of the Congregational minister of Whitfield's Tabernacle, Moorfields, felt strangely moved. Indeed, *she* herself would go and join the throng. She looked across to where the tall young man, Gottlob Schreiner, was singing earnestly. . . . He had recently left Islington College to join the London Missionary Society. Her eyes softened with tenderness. Gottlob had asked her to marry him, and go with him to Africa to serve God by teaching the heathen their ways. . . . That night she told Gottlob, the German student from Basel, that she would marry him. She knew that he was one of the many sons of a shoemaker, who had lived in Fellbach near Stuttgart, and that he was a poor man, but that did not deter her.

It was of this union that Olive Emilie Albertina Schreiner was born on March 24, 1855, at the Native Reserve Mission Station of Wittebergen on the border of Basutoland. She was the ninth child of Rebecca Lyndall, a profoundly English wife, and Gottlob Schreiner. The young couple had sailed for South Africa under orders of the London Missionary Society shortly after Queen Victoria had come to the throne of England. Always Olive regarded herself as an English South African, as distinguished from the Boers, notwithstanding the fact that her childhood was spent on mission stations in the Boer section of the country. In the home in which she grew up, only English was allowed to be

spoken. Her mother was utterly insistent in this matter. Nevertheless, Olive learned the Afrikaans tongue, which at this time
was a somewhat simple and limited language. One day, when
Olive was six years old, she was swinging on the door, looking
at the landscape bathed in the intensive karroo sunshine, as she
remarked, "Ach, how lovely it is outside." The use of the slang
expression angered her mother, who punished her by beating her
bare body. It just may be that what developed in Olive as a fierce
reaction against all forms of physical violence had its roots in
such traumatic experiences. It was a double reaction, against
both the intolerance in the matter of the Afrikaans language,
making it more attractive, and the powerlessness of violence to
change the mind and alter the behavior pattern of people.

Certain very crucial influences in her life cast long shafts of
light, making luminous the entire landscape of her maturity.
Some of these have been indicated in the preceding pages of this
essay. But let us get them totally in perspective. Her mother was
a strong, positive, declarative person. When she came to South
Africa, she was full of high hopes and enthusiasm that belonged
to a sensitive person caught up in the spirit of adventure defined
in terms of the evangelical fervor of her husband. There is general agreement that she did not ever recover from the shock of
the initial impact of the deep isolation and barrenness of the
section of the country in which she and her husband settled. They
were placed in a vast barren area far removed from the cultural
influences of life as she had known them in her native land. The
area was remote, and companions of the mind and spirit were not
to be found. Under the sharp glare of the African sun, the primitive life of the Boers in their general surroundings, the life of a
missionary among African natives—these conspired together to
build a windbreak behind which she had to rear her own family.
It seems clear from the records that she could not find refuge in
a simple religious faith that would immunize her against the

ravages of her environment. The sense of mission, so fundamental to the evangelical enterprise, could not meet her need as a person, a missionary, and a mother. She had to be utterly resourceful to find ways for keeping her family healthy in the strange and enervating climate. It is not surprising that there are those who pinpoint Olive Schreiner's lifelong interest in medicine not only to her own personal struggle for health but also to the fact that her mother must have pored over a general medical book to be found in every missionary home of the period. In such an early environment, one can see the seeds that will grow and blossom in the later life of this strange and talented woman.

Of formal training, there was little. Under the circumstances it had to be given by her mother, because her father had to carry the wider responsibilities of his mission work. As her mother was the formal and cultured Englishwoman, soon disenchanted with the evangelical fervor that had sent her and her husband on the long trek to save and redeem the African, her father was the man of gentle piety, with a heart always open to the needs of his fellows. One of Olive Schreiner's biographers gives a sharply focused portrait of Olive's father, as quoted by Edward Carpenter in his autobiography:

Olive herself has often told me how he would give away his last coin to anyone he deemed to be in need. His wife would say to him: (The name John is a liberty used by Carpenter) "John, where is that best Sunday coat of yours?"

And he would say: "Is it not upstairs in the chest as usual?"

"No, John, I have been looking for it everywhere."

"How very strange," was the reply. "No, surely, my dear, I could not have given *that* away—at least I think not."

"John! Now tell me true, did you not give it to that *tramp* that came yesterday?"

"Well, my dear, now you mention it, I think I may have done so; it is just possible. You are right, but I am sure I hardly remember."

"Oh, John! John! You are indeed incorrigible.[1]

The biographer goes on to say: "That was the picture of the father—soft, pitiful, and dreamy. The mother, Rebecca Lyndall by her maiden name, was of English descent, keen, intellectual, fine-featured and somewhat self-willed. The two types were combined in their daughter." Olive Schreiner's life was greatly affected by a lifelong battle for health. Very early in her life she was harassed by a chronic asthmatic condition, precipitated, according to some of her contemporaries, by exposure on a long journey in an ox cart during the rainy season. Be that as it may, the simple fact is that until her death she was scarcely ever free from the discomfort of and often acute suffering from this respiratory condition. The fact often determined where she lived and for how long a time. Sometimes it seemed as if she would find a cure—in South Africa, in England, and in Europe—but, in the end, there was none. In the light of what is known today about the causes of asthma, as rooted often in tension created by a highly sensitive nervous system, the source of Olive Schreiner's chronic condition may have been due to the way she was internally organized. She was sensitive, highly keyed, subject to states of euphoria and depression. One is moved with compassion for her as she wandered from place to place, always at the mercy of an internal agitation. Her unrest was rooted sometimes in the condition of her health and other times in her response to the existential factors which created the world of men and affairs in which she lived and of which she was a part. At any rate, it seems clear that for a person with such a refined quality of sensitivity to life, and the necessity for coping with a debilitating and exhausting drain upon energy, life would be one sustained agony. One of the ways to cope with such a problem would be to generate,

1. D. L. Hobman, *Olive Schreiner: Her Friends and Times*, pp. 28–29.

perhaps unconsciously, waves of energy capable of sustaining the concentration of thought and action.

From her photographs and from various descriptions of her, Olive was very striking, with a compelling magnetism radiating from her personality. The solitary, isolated farm on which she lived during both her girlhood and youth, as well as during much of her later years after her marriage, had a profound influence on the very sinews of her thought. Her writings are invaded by a sense of vastness and timelessness. There seems to be a built-in tendency for people to correspond with their environments. Moments there are when the boundaries of the self from within which one "deals" with the environment seem to fade and reappear, fade and reappear. This interaction may easily become the rhythm of life. One is invaded by the environment rather than merely internalizing it. With Olive Schreiner, throughout her life, there were islands of urban living, whether in South Africa or England, contained in the vast, dynamic solitariness of the karroo or the isolated farmhouse hard by a lonely railway crossing. One senses in her the long loneliness that is on the other side of sadness or melancholy but from which she brings the rich, ripe fruit of her emotional creativity. Even when her health was poorest and her energy scarcely marginal, she could focus with glowing eyes and a flood of language, calling upon her deep, hidden resources to champion some cause or to make the abiding statement.

But what were her other resources? From time to time there came into her hands many seminal books, which she read with great hunger and insight. Among them were Spencer's *First Principles*, Emerson's *Essays*, Edward Carpenter's *Love's Coming of Age* and *Towards Democracy*; but above all, the Bible. She had a most intimate and primary acquaintance with this book; perhaps more than any other book, it influenced her style, her thought, and her insights. Anyone acquainted with the King James Version of the

Bible will recognize at once the unconscious bearing that this book had on her manner of phrasing. It seems that the biblical style was far more influential than its religious teaching. And yet this is not quite accurate. One of the most revealing accounts of her childhood has to do with her reaction upon first reading the Sermon on the Mount. She ran into the room where her mother was talking with friends and, with utter enthusiasm, exclaimed, "I have known all along that this is the way we are supposed to live." Her mother's reaction was direct. Olive not only was rebuffed but also was severely punished on a "bare body." It is impossible to know what subtle inner process was precipitated in Olive which resulted finally in her later disenchantment with the Christian religion. Adults are scarcely aware of the utter vulnerability of children.

The reader who is acquainted with the life of Olive Schreiner will observe that my introductory essay omits certain aspects of her life that are central to her story. For example, there is scarcely a reference to her long and beautiful friendship with Havelock Ellis. These omissions are intentional, because the scope of my undertaking limits me to what in my judgment would most easily acquaint the reader with how the woman's mind worked and how she reacted to the broad urgencies of her day. Those who wish to pursue the study of her life in depth will find substantive material in Cronwright-Schreiner's *Life of Olive Schreiner* and *The Letters of Olive Schreiner* and in several books written in observance of the 1955 centennial of her birth. My choice among the latter is *Not Without Honour, The Life and Writings of Olive Schreiner*, by Vera Buchanan-Gould.

It is difficult to identify precisely the influences that shape and fashion the life of an individual. The enigma is the process at work in the private world of an individual that finds its expression in the thoughts, words, and actions that ultimately emerge. It has been aptly said that the time and place of a man's life is the time and place of his body, but the meaning and significance of a man's life is as creative, as vast, and as far-reaching as his gifts, his dreams, and his response to his times can make them. This was certainly true of Olive Schreiner. In fine, here is a sensitive, poetic, compassionate woman who, due to the accident of birth and heritage, came into the world in South Africa. It was a time that antedated the formation of the Union of South Africa, made up of English, Boer, Huguenot, and indigenous Africans. It was a time of great antagonisms between the English and the Boers, eventuating finally in the Boer War, which turned the country into violent ferment and conflict. It was a sharp and piercing conflict—the English, on the one hand, were transplants and colonizers, with their roots firmly grounded in English soil. They were spiritually alien to the land and, in a most significant sense, had never left England. A stretch of years had to make up the interval before South Africa, in truth, would be the homeland of the spirit. Even today there is this mood left and sensed as one encounters the Englishman whose total life has been spent in what was once a part of the developing British Empire. In my travels, I have seen fewer sadder expressions of muted longing than the sight of several hundred Australians standing on the dock as a ship pulled out into the channel, turning its bow to the open sea and England. They, for the most part, were people born in Australia, many of whom had never seen the "homeland." They seemed like alien corn in strange, unyielding soil.

Then there were the Boers who regarded South Africa as their true homeland. There seemed to have been a weird messianism in their fervor. They were not establishing a home away from home, with the smell of their native hearth forever hot in their nostrils. No. They were in their place, "set apart for them by God" and established there through the working of his implacable will. They had no choice but to obey. The land, the Africans, the sky, the life—all these were there, placed by their God to succor and nourish them in the fulfillment of a divine promise.

Chief among the indigenous, or so-called native, peoples was the strong, verile, authentic Bantu. In her pamphlet *Closer Union*, written in 1908, Olive Schreiner says of him:

He has never been subjected to the dissolving and desocializing ordeal of slavery. We find him in the land of his growth with all the instincts of the free man intact; with all the instincts of loyalty to his race and its chief warm in his heart; with his social instincts almost abnormally developed and fully active; we have only with wisdom and patient justice slowly to transfer them to our larger society—they are there! Every man and woman who has studied the Bantu in his native state—before we have indoctrinated him with those vices which dog everywhere the feet of our civilization, and have compelled his women to graduate in our brothels and his men in our canteens or have dragged him into our city slums, where even our own races rot—knows that the proudest of us may envy many of the social virtues which the Bantu displays.[2]

In connection with the African peoples themselves there is revealed the subtle conflict which was never quite resolved by Olive Schreiner. In contemporary language, she was not an avowed racist, as was Rhodes and his like; she was not a messianic racist, as were the Boers; nor was she a religious racist, as was the dominant missionary mood of the period. She was, by endowment and philosophy, a universalist in outlook and feeling, while, at the same time, being a child of her times as a member of the exploiting and colonizing community. This created a moral paradox, which is expressed dramatically in her story of Peter Halket, to which reference will be made subsequently.

Add to all of this the discovery of unlimited mineral wealth—gold and diamonds—and the tidal wave of greed and mayhem that this calls forth from the very bowels of "civilized" men. The central and pivotal genius who moves to the center of the stage

2. *Closer Union*, Letter to "Transvaal Leader," October 30, 1908, pp. 47–48.

was Cecil John Rhodes (1853–1902). It is very easy to go astray and bog down in the details and the complexities of that strange admixture of daring vision, courage, and ruthlessness that surrounds this builder of an empire and the fashioner of the destiny of the country down to latest times. Not surprisingly, there was an utter attraction felt between him and Olive Schreiner. Much has been written about this relationship, and here I must touch upon the moment in history which brought them together.

Rhodes and Olive Schreiner were the most outstanding and challenging figures of the period. They towered above their fellows by all accounting, and yet the very grain in their wood sent their lives spinning in opposite directions. It is quite possible that the *feel* for the land, the sweep of the karroo and the velt, which in *The Story of An African Farm* sometimes dwarfs the characters of the novel, made a compelling appeal to the mind of Rhodes. It is recorded that he carried a copy of the book in his pocket. Yet Olive Schreiner was interested in people and what could be done to help them actualize their potential. Rhodes was interested in himself and the expanding colonial empire of Britain. It was the land and its vast resources, waiting to be exploited and converted into wealth and power, that rallied all the talents of this powerful, ruthless, lonely man.

We see in Olive Schreiner's attitude a cruel ambivalence. It is set forth in a skit which she called "The Salvation of a Ministry." In her allegory, she is in heaven, seated in the balcony. There is very little happening, because few people are coming up from earth. Various people appear from South Africa, concerning whom God wanted the recording angel to answer one question, one question only: What was this man's position on the Stropping Bill? This was a bill which gave the landowner the right to whip the African if he did not work hard enough. If a man supported the bill, he was at once consigned to hell.

When Rhodes came before the judge, it was announced that

not only did he support the bill but he sired it. "Take him to hell" were the dreadful words. The allegory continues:

I could smell the great gridirons in hell heating and the fat in the pans warming for him, even in heaven.

God sat silent.

After a little time we heard a great noise; a rushing and tumbling; it was all the devils in hell coming up again, and they were bringing C. R. with them.

And the devils were draggling their tails on the ground, and their mouths were hanging open.

God said, "How is this? Why have you brought him back again? Did I not give him to you to damn?"

And the devils said, "Oh, Lord God, we tried to damn him. We took him to the great front door, but when we got him there he stuck fast in it. We pushed and we pulled, but we couldn't get him through; he was too large for it."

God said, "Why did you not try some other way?"

The devils said, "Lord God, we took him round to all the doors and windows in hell, but there was not one big enough for him to get through. It would have brought all hell down, if we had tried. You made him too great for us!"

And God turned, he said, "Bring my son here! There is no room for him anywhere but in heaven."[3]

Cronwright-Schreiner writes that Olive told him of an exchange with Rhodes on one occasion. "Why do you surround yourself with the type of men you do? Why do you make friends of such men?" She said that Rhodes flew into a towering rage and violently and contemptuously replied, "*Those* men my friends! They are not my *friends*. They are my tools, and when I have done with them I throw them away." Further, he says that she insisted that Rhodes had said: "I prefer land to niggers."[4]

3. Quoted in S. C. Cronwright-Schreiner, *The Life of Olive Schreiner*, p. 202.
4. *The Life of Olive Schreiner*, pp. 214 ff.

It is out of her explosive rejection of Rhodes and all he symbolized in South Africa that Olive Schreiner wrote *Trooper Peter Halket of Mashonaland.* The year of its publication was 1897. On the first page of this book there is a bitter photograph—a large tree with sturdy limbs, a little less in diameter than the trunk itself. From these limbs are the dead bodies of three Africans hanging in the breeze. Standing nonchalantly around are ten white men responsible for the macabre scene of lynch law. It is a dramatic introduction to the terrible unfolding of brutality that is revealed in the story as the true foundation of the British Empire built upon the writhing agony of nameless Africans, whose number is legion.

What of the story itself? It is a tale of a certain private of the Chartered Company of Mashonaland. When he is sent out as a scout, he becomes separated from his company. He is lost. As night falls, he builds a fire for warmth and company and to give certain protection from marauding wild animals. The intimate stillness of the great silence of the African night invades him totally. His mind is free now to roam over the days of his childhood; he remembers his mother and all the vicissitudes of growing up in the English village where these early years were spent. His story continues to unfold through the experiences in South Africa, the Chartered Company, his fantasies of what he will do when his term of service is over and he is given his share of the land taken from the Mashonas and the Matabeles. He foresees a time when the law of the Chartered Company would make it legal for black men to be compelled to work for white men. On and on the fantasy unfolds. In this reverie he hears the quiet footsteps of someone approaching. He calls out in fear. There emerges in the firelight a barefoot Jew from Palestine. Upon inquiry, Peter discovers that he is not of the Chartered Company, but he is a strange man, with calm countenance and a strong point of view.

When Peter finds out that the stranger is not interested in gold, diamonds, and land, he wonders aloud as to what the man is up to. It is here that the drama begins to mount, for Peter exclaims, "If you don't want to make money, why do you come here?" Now Peter is faced with an utterly new experience. The stranger says that his company consists of men of many nations and races. He is not with one people more than another. In fact, in his company there are men and women of every class, race, nation, and religion. "It matters to us nothing by what name the man is named, so he is one of us."

In the dialogue between Peter and the stranger, much of Olive Schreiner's basic social philosophy and humanitarian graces are voiced. The selections that follow include ample quotations from this book, setting forth her ideas in texts. The stranger gives a series of messages which he asks Peter to take back to England or to give to the people of South Africa itself. These messages contain very revealing commentary on what is taking place in the contemporary scene. But Peter feels inadequate and unworthy. If all else fails, the stranger urges Peter to take the message to himself. "Say, 'I, Peter Halket, sinner among you all, who have desired women and gold, who have loved myself and hates my fellows I—' The Stranger looked down at him, and placed his hand gently on his head. 'Peter Simon Halket,' he said, 'a harder task I give you than any which has been laid upon you. In that small spot where alone on earth your will rules, bring there into being the kingdom to-day. Love your enemies; do good to them that hate you. Walk ever forward, looking not to the right hand or the left. Heed not what men shall say of you. Succour the oppressed; deliver the captive. If thine enemy hunger, feed him; if he is athirst, give him drink.' A curious warmth and gladness stole over Peter Halket as he knelt; it was as when a little child his mother folded him to her: he saw nothing more about him but a soft bright light. Yet in it he heard a voice cry, 'Because thou hast loved mercy—and hated oppression!—' "[5]

5. *Trooper Peter Halket of Mashonaland*, p. 93.

At length, the stranger leaves, and Peter returns to his company, a changed and purged man—how changed and how purged he himself scarcely knows.

An earlier reference has been made to Olive Schreiner and the so-called native question. It is appropriate to explore this at greater depth in order that more insight may be gained into her own life and meaning. I stated that her attitude was in sharp contrast with that of Rhodes. This was due not merely to the fact that she was not a man fashioning an empire, spreading the "glory" of the white man's civilization and culture among the heathen. True, she was born of missionaries in a missionary family. But, like her father, she seemed disposed to identify more with the Africans themselves than with their predicament. She was acutely involved in their plight, but she was that rare person who was able to project herself into the life of the individual, locate him securely, and then inform herself as to how it felt to see the view from the other side. I think this is a direct influence of her father on her life, in addition to the insight referred to earlier in this essay.

When I first began reading her books and had passed beyond my skepticism concerning her because she was a South African white woman, it was necessary for me to find out for myself what her real attitude toward the Africans themselves was. First of all, it became clear to me that she was not concerned about Christianizing them. However this may seem, and I do not say it either carelessly or irreverently, she did not love the Africans for Christ's sake. Therefore, as a black man, I could deal with her attitude with integrity. In all of her utterances, she seemed to escape the necessity of thinking of the African in abstract rather than in concrete terms. And yet I found myself alerted to what seemed to be a kind of sentimentality. I suppose what I am saying is that I had to overcome certain well-grounded prejudices that screened everything I read from her life. I was profoundly moved and stirred by the power of her creative imagery. It was enough for me that somewhere, and at sometime, there had lived a person with such gifts. But when I placed her in her setting, my problems arose.

In reading her books, I discovered that fundamental to her attitude toward people in general and Africans in particular, she was a woman concerned about the condition and position of women in the world. A little later this fact will be enlarged upon. It is sufficient merely to say here that being a woman with such a personal concern at once broadened the base of her awareness of injustices, discrimination, and suffering. Further, she was English, with an acute sense of history. She felt a loyalty to those values which to her satisfaction marked the true distinction of the Englishman. Listen to what she says about the uniqueness of the Englishman:

> The majority of Englishmen love freedom, but they love it in three different ways. The majority love it as a possession for themselves alone; they will not be interfered with, nor will they have their freedom of action barred by anyone or anything; they are not careful of the freedom of others, nor are they at all reluctant to sacrifice and annihilate it if it increases their own. . . .
>
> This love of freedom the Englishman shares with most savage and nomadic peoples; it is found in almost the highest perfection in the South African Boer. . . .
>
> There are a large number of us, though small compared to the first class, who love freedom for ourselves but also do not desire to grasp our liberty at the cost of others. We love liberty so dearly that we would not willingly inflict an injustice or a wrong on another, and we respect the freedom of others while we venerate our own. . . . It is a high and great, a noble quality, but I do not think it makes us unique among the people of the world.
>
> But there is yet a third way in which some of us love freedom. . . . We love freedom not only for ourselves, but we desire with a burning passion to spread it broadcast over the earth; to see every human being safeguarded by it and raised to the level at which they may enjoy it; we

desire freedom not only for ourselves but for humanity; and we labour to spread it. *This*, I hold, is the one great gift which England and England alone possesses; this is the quality which makes us unique among the nations of the earth; this is the gift which we have to contribute to the great common offertory of humanity.[6]

In order to deal fairly with her total position, I must add a further quotation:

Some nations have set their slaves free, but only our English race speaking the English tongue and imbued with English ideals has shed its blood for them! This is a new thing under the sun. . . . This never happened before. It is a new era. We know, none so well, how stained is our African record; we know with what envious eyes the Government of English Ahabs eyes the patrimony of Black Naboths and takes it, if necessary, after bearing false witness against Naboth; we know how Englishmen have crossed the continent and left behind them a trail of slime and gore such as few Arabic slave caravans leave; but we know that, with hearts full of soft concern for its inhabitants, and all the tenderness of strength and wisdom, Englishmen have trodden this continent and laboured among its lowest people; not Livingstone alone but a great corps of lesser unrecorded Livingstones whose names will be forgotten, but the fruits of whose lives will abide.[7]

And finally, she possessed what comes through to me as an innate, instinctual sense of the unity of all of life. It was this emphasis in her writing that was the first external confirmation of what had always been an active ingredient in my own awareness of life. As a boy in Florida, I walked along the beach of the Atlantic in the quiet stillness that can only be completely felt when the murmur of the ocean is stilled and the tides move stealthily along the shore. I held my breath against the night and watched the stars etch their brightness on the face of the dark-

6. *Thoughts on South Africa*, pp. 342–343.
7. Ibid., p. 345.

ened canopy of the heavens. I had the sense that all things, the sand, the sea, the stars, the night, and I were *one* lung through which all of life breathed. Not only was I aware of a vast rhythm enveloping all, but I was a part of it and it was a part of me. It was not until I read Olive Schreiner that I was able to establish sufficient psychological distance between me and the totality of such experiences to make the experience itself an object of thought. Thus it became possible for me to move from primary experience, to conceptualizing that experience, to a vision inclusive of all of life. The resulting creative synthesis was to me *religious* rather than *metaphysical,* as seems to have been true in Olive Schreiner's case.

The reader will observe in this anthology a wide range of selections, stating and restating the theme of the unity of life. Her husband reproduces from memory what Olive said to him concerning her thought on this point.

All matter is alive, even so-called inanimate matter; a stone has no apparent energy and so *seems* dead; but life runs through everything. Wherever there is *life,* the laws of the universe are functioning. As life is not manifest in "inanimate" things, we cannot perceive these laws at work as we can see them in more energized, more highly organized, matter. The laws of the universe manifest themselves more and more perfectly in proportion to the higher organization of the matter, and so on, up the scale, till the brain of man is reached; there they are working in greater perfection than in any other part of matter; in the mind of *genius,* however, they are manifested in still higher perfection, in proportion to the genius and the direction in which it functions; genius *knows* things; it does not need to argue, nor does it need proof, because the laws of the brain of genius are the laws of the cosmos working more perfectly than in other brains; genius, in expressing itself, is but correctly expressing the laws of the cosmos.[8]

8. *The Life of Olive Schreiner,* p. 223.

Despite this fundamental affirmation about the unity of life and the resultant compassion for all of life which it inspired, it was not easy for her to translate these into the terms of a primary attitude toward the individual African. As has been commented upon earlier, in certain ways she was a part of her context as a South African woman. I shall never forget my shock and anger when, in some of her stories or other writings, the word *nigger* was used. I do not refer to the times when she is quoting someone like Rhodes, or when it is a part of the language of one of the characters in her story, as in *Trooper Peter Halket*. Even though such a term was a part of the common language of the Boer and the English, for Olive Schreiner to be guilty of such insensitivity seemed to me inexcusably obscene. To the reader, this may seem undue sensitiveness on my part. So be it.

Olive Schreiner was a pacifist. The logic of her world view made this inevitable. She was opposed to the Boer War not merely upon political and psychological grounds, but also because of her basic view of life. Her reasons for opposing this war, as well as the First World War, may be casually interpreted as objections to these particular wars. But this is to take a superficial view of her position. Her attitude caused her much suffering both in her native land and in England, and in Italy during her sojourns there.

Let us take a closer look at the grounds of her pacifism as stated in an article, "The Dawn of Civilization," which appeared in *The London Nation and Athenaeum* on March 26, 1921. The first half of the article examines the three ways by which an individual may conscientiously object to war.

First, he may inherit from his forebears the position that war is an "evil not to be trafficked with." Even though his fellows may be in disagreement with him, they can understand the significance of the heritage transmitted to him in that way. Upon reflection, they realize that most of them accept their politics and religion as a matter of inheritance, first of all. Such a man may be punished for his views, yet those who punish will understand "how he got that way."

Second, he may object, in all good conscience, to a particular war for some definite and limited reason. During any given war there may be those who have convictions about the wrongness of the war in which the nation is engulfed. "He may believe the war to have been led up to by a false and mad diplomacy, to be based upon a mistaken judgment of the national interests; and therefore he may feel compelled to oppose the particular war while the bulk of men and women in his society desire and approve it." Such a man may hope by his witness to cause an increasing number of his fellows to believe and to think as he believes and thinks. His society may disagree with him, but all thoughtful men could understand how he might arrive at his position, and thus to that extent identify with him and exercise a measured tolerance toward him.

Third, he may object to war in radically different ways. "His objection . . . may not be based on any hereditary tradition, or on the teaching of any organized society, or of any of the great historic figures of the past. . . . He may fully recognize the difference in type between one war and another; between a war for dominance, trade expansion, or the maintenance of Empire, and a war in which a class or a race struggles against a power seeking permanently to crush and subject it, or in which a man fights in the land of his birth for the soil on which he first saw light, against the stranger seeking to dispossess him." Nevertheless, a man may hold that no gain inferred by war can compensate for the evils which result. "He is unable to assist not merely in the actual carnage of war, but, as far as possible, in all that leads to its success." There is no necessity for such a man to belong to any organized religion or to base his convictions on some moral or even aesthetic teaching. He may arrive at his position as a part of his total response to life and his experience of it.

I think that it was the latter position which characterized Olive Schreiner's objection to war. Indeed, in her article she makes the point that the "personal element" enters fully into the statement of her pacifism. For this she is somewhat apologetic, while at the same time making it clear why she must regard herself as a "universal conscientious objector to war."

In part 2 of the article, Olive Schreiner undertakes to establish the grounds of her position in her own fact. She makes clear that it is her total yet personal response to the existential circumstances of her life. It is helpful in our understanding of her to enter into the explanation or rationalization of the way she saw her world and what, in her terms, were her responses to it. Her responses became a way of looking out upon the total landscape of her life for the garnering of meaning, which has been passed on to us. It is these elements with which she deals in part 2 of her discussion.

She says that she had grown up in a land in which wars were common. She had seen during the most formative period of her life how white men fought white men and how white men had used black men as beasts of burden with no thought of their good or happiness. On three occasions she had seen an ox trying to pull a heavy load up a hill, the blood and foam streaming from its mouth and nostrils until it fell dead under the lash. She had seen animals killed just for the sport of it. Always there were convicts with chains around their waists which passed between their legs to irons on their feet. She ached to give them succor and to let them know that somebody loved them, that somebody cared. Again and again she asked herself, "Why do the strong always crush the weak? Why do we hate and kill and torture? Why was it all as it was? Why had the world ever been made? O, why had I ever been born?"

And what is her answer? It is in terms of a vivid sense of personal responsibility that from one point of view seems melodramatic, sentimental, and perhaps even neurotic. But who is to say, and by what canon of judgment? We will hear what she says:

> You cannot by willing it alter the vast world outside of you; you cannot, perhaps, cut the lash from one whip; you cannot, perhaps, strike the handcuffs from one chained hand; you cannot even remake your own soul so that there shall be no tendency to evil in it; the great world rolls on, and *you* cannot reshape it; but this one thing you can do—in that one, small, minute almost infinitesimal spot in the Universe, where your will rules, there, where alone you are as God, *strive* to make what you hunger for real! . . . In your own heart strive to kill out all hate, all desire to see evil come even to those who have injured you or another; what is weaker than yourself try to help; whatever is in pain or unjustly treated and cries out, say, "I am here! I, little, weak, feeble, but I will do what I can for you." This is all you can do; but do it; it is not nothing! And then this feeling came to me, a feeling it is not easy to put into words, but it was like this: You also are a part of the great universe; what you strive for something strives for; and *nothing in this universe is quite alone;* you are moving on toward something.

This vision Olive Schreiner carried with her through all the years of her living. "That which was for the young child a vision, a flash of almost blinding light, which it could hardly even to itself translate, has, in the course of a long life's experience, become a hope, which I think the cool reason can find grounds to justify, and which a growing knowledge of human nature and human life does endorse. Somehow, somewhere, some place—even on earth."

It remains now to examine the bearing of Olive Schreiner's outlook on the relation between men and women. As an indication of the general social climate of the Western world in which she lived, it is only necessary to observe that when she published her first book, *The Story of An African Farm,* she thought it necessary to use a pseudonym, Ralph Iron. This is a clear indication of the place of women in the world of the nineteenth century. It is true that in subsequent editions she used her real name, but the initial fact is most telling. As a full-orbed recognition of her thought and feelings in this matter, when she married, her husband took her last name hyphenated with his—Cronwright-Schreiner.

She was a pioneer in the women's movement, but she was not unwomanly. I have found no evidence in my research which indicated even by inference that she was not utterly feminine. The earliest photographs show her to be not only an attractive but also an authentic woman, with a gentle beauty and a gathered winsomeness. Her essential dynamism appealed to and enveloped men in its spell. An independence about her manifested itself not only in the bold, audacious working of her mind but also in matters of more intimate and personal choices. She did not believe in women binding their bodies in stays, and she smoked cigarettes. Concerning marriage, she once said to Edward Carpenter, "If the world requires a legal ceremony, go through with it; just as you walk on the pavement instead of the middle of the street, if your fellow-men demand it. What does matter is that both persons should be sure that they love each other with a deathless love which no other human being should be able to undo, and that the woman be absolutely and entirely monetarily *independent of the man.* That is the great thing; let love bind you, not a common bank account. . . . I think it to be the most holy, the most organic, the most important sacrament in life; and how men and women can enter into it with the light-hearted indifference they do, has always been, and is, a matter of endless wonder to me."

Her identification with the exploited and depressed, in addition to her feeling as a woman in a man-dominated world, seems to have been at work in her interpretation of what it means to be a woman. In her book, *Woman and Labor,* selections from which appear in the Reader, she states her position and defines the essential problem of being a woman in the nineteenth century. This book was published in 1911. According to the introduction, it is a summary of a much longer and more comprehensive work which was destroyed by fire during the Boer War when she was forced to vacate her premises. She lays the groundwork for her discussion by insisting that women of no race or class will rise up in revolt against their condition, however awful their condition may be, so long as the welfare of the total society demands that they remain in submission. When women revolt, it is always a sure indication that their role as defined in the society is no longer necessary. There seems to be a sense of responsibility for the total well-being of society always present in the psychic style of women, which takes precedence over their own comfort and well-being. In other words, the active concern for freedom on the part of women can be understood only against the background of a larger concept, namely, freedom is pursued only when to achieve it is not to threaten or destroy the fabric of society. There is a responsibility which transcends the demands of freedom, and that is the well-being of the life which is made possible through her loins. This attitude bristles with ambiquities which may clear up as her position is more clearly defined.

Olive Schreiner's thesis is that in the evolution of society the function of woman has been steadily narrowed. The time when she shared in the work that kept the community viable, as well as bore the children, has passed, and in the modern world women are reduced to parasitism. The curse of the age for women is the fact that they are forced to be parasites in the society. They no longer share in the work of maintaining the common life. Little by little they have been forced into a tight circle to perform the only service which by nature cannot be taken from them—bearers of the children of the society. It is summarized by her as follows: "We demand that, in that strange new world that is arising alike upon the man and the woman, where nothing is as it was, and all

things are assuming new shapes and relations, that in this new
world we also shall have our share of honored and socially useful
human toil, our full half of the labor of the children of woman.
We demand nothing more than this, and we will take nothing
less. This is our WOMAN'S RIGHT!"[9] This could have been written
today—it has a familiar contemporary ring to it.

The substitution of mechanical force for human labor, which
is creating chaos for the workers of the world, is having an even
more deadly effect upon the life of women. One by one in the
division of labor to keep society functioning, the conventional
work of woman is steadily being eliminated. While, at the same
time, there is vast reluctance to swing wide the door for her
entrance into useful work hitherto reserved for men only. The
logic of the attitude is to have the function of women limited to
the sexual experience of life. As the standard of living rises, the
sexual role of woman becomes less and less involved in the bearing of children, and her function becomes more and more exclu-
sively sexual. When her role is confined to that narrow area
without the overall sense of contribution to the life stream that
bearing children indicates, in essence, she becomes a prostitute
—the parasite par excellence.

In Olive Schreiner's thought, the women's movement is essentially a labor movement. Again and again she discusses the men's
labor movement of her day as "two streams rising from one
fountainhead.[10] However, she makes an interesting seminal distinction between them: the male labor movement *takes its rise*
mainly among the poor and hard-laboring classes; while the
women's labor movement has risen primarily among the cultured, sophisticated, and brain-laboring classes where, according
to her, is "the present day danger . . . of degeneration through

9. *Woman and Labor,* p. 65.
10. *Woman and Labor,* p. 122.

dependence upon the sex function." She sees the latter movement as an effort of a section of the race to save itself from
inactivity and degeneration.

Olive Schreiner insists that women take all labor as their province, and this of necessity includes war. She asks the question

"What then of war, that struggle of the human creature to attain its ends
by physical force and at the price of the life of others: will you take part
in that also?" We reply: Yes; more particularly in that field we intend to
play our part. We have always borne part of the weight of war, and the
major part. It is not that in primitive times we suffered from the destruction of the fields we tilled and the houses we built . . . it is not that in
a comparatively insignificant manner, as nurses of the wounded in modern times . . . we have borne our part; nor is it even because the spirit
of resolution in its women, and their willingness to endure, has in all
ages . . . determined the fate of a race that goes to war, that we demand
our controlling right where war is concerned. Our relation to war is far
more intimate, personal, and indissoluble than this. Men have made
boomerangs, bows, swords, or guns with which to destroy one another;
we have made the men who destroyed and were destroyed! . . . There
is no battlefield on earth, nor ever has been, howsoever covered with
slain, which it has not cost the women of the race more in actual bloodshed and anguish to supply, then it has cost the men who lie there. *We
pay the first cost on all human life.*[11]

We have come full circle. Here is a woman, born in South
Africa in the middle of the nineteenth century. Her parents were
missionaries—the father, German, quiet, pious, dedicated, compassionate, and effective only in one-to-one relationships; the
mother, English, brilliant, sophisticated, and rebellious against
her role as the wife of a missionary. One of nine children, Olive's
formal education was practically nil, her temperament mercurial;
she was superbly gifted, with a mind that ranged over vast areas

11. *Woman and Labor,* pp. 173–174.

of human thought and knowledge, yet profoundly frustrated by a chronic, debilitating disease; she was solitary, brooding, with a sensitivity to all forms of injustice and human suffering—a brilliant, scintillating imagination, intolerant of anything that encircled or imprisoned the body, the spirit, or the mind. One by one, her ambitions, whether to study medicine, to teach, to bear many children, were blocked. Her marriage came comparatively late in life—the one child lived only a matter of hours—to a husband who was somewhat stolid, pedestrian, honest, and courageous, who was willing to make concession to her genius, even to taking her name as part of his and subjugating his life as a responsible husband to both her urgencies and her whims. Her tragedy was the fact that she had a "masculine" mind, with all the emotional depth of a profoundly feeling, articulate woman. She was honored and feted as a superbly sensitive writer by some of the finest minds in both Englind and her native South Africa; she saw many of them turn against her because of her attitude toward war. Again and again, life stripped her of the assurance of a conventional religious faith, of the reassurance that comes from having the uncritical attitude toward imperialism with all that that implies in an expanding colonialism, of the sense of belonging to her sex, which made of her a pioneer in the movement for freedom of women—all these, and much more, narrowed the circle of her life until she was utterly at the mercy of a crushing illness, leaving her to die alone and broken on December 16, 1920. She and her baby, and now her husband, are buried in a sarcophagus on the summit of Buffels Kop in South Africa.

The Cradock newspaper, *The Midland News,* of August 17, 1921, has the following report of her burial: "Mr. Cronwright-Schreiner . . . said it was not Olive Schreiner that lay in the largest coffin; it was but the time-garment which, for a brief space, had been the dwelling of that holy and exquisite spirit.

. . . He ended by repeating, with almost breaking intensity, a sweet verse from Tennyson's 'In Memoriam':

> Thy voice is on the rolling air;
> I hear thee where the waters run;
> Thou standest in the rising sun,
> And in the setting thou art fair.

"There was no other ceremony. No fence encloses the margin of land on which the sarcophagus stands; it is surrounded by the wild life she loved and in view of the mountains that have no end."

The selections that make up the Reader begin with Olive Schreiner's first book, *The Story of An African Farm*, on the basis of which her fame initially rests. It is her best known and most lasting literary contribution. In these selections, as in all the others which follow, my aim has been to make choices which seem to me to stand by themselves and in their own right. The contextual meaning of the passages has been largely ignored. For more than twenty-five years, I have read many of these selections to groups of all kinds, in many parts of the United States and the world. There is a timeless effectiveness which goes straight to the aspirations, feeling tones, and dreams of the human spirit. Many of the selections have nourished my spirit in strange and defiant ways. May the reader find here and there that which speaks to his condition and gives wings to his mind and heart.

BIBLIOGRAPHY

Buchanan-Gould, Vera. *Not Without Honour, The Life and Writings of Olive Schreiner.* With an introduction by Field Marshal, The Rt. Hon. J. C. Smuts. London: Hutchinson, n.d.

Cronwright-Schreiner, Samuel Cron. *The Letters of Olive Schreiner.* London: T. Fisher Unwin, 1924.

————. *The Life of Olive Schreiner.* Boston: Little, Brown, and Co., n.d.

Gregg, Lyndall (Dot Schreiner). *Memories of Olive Schreiner.* London and Edinburgh: W. & R. Chambers, 1957.

Hobman, D. L. *Olive Schreiner. Her Friends and Times.* London: Watts, 1955.

SOURCES OF SELECTIONS

Dreams. Boston: Little, Brown, and Co., 1900.

From Man to Man; or Perhaps only . . . (with an introduction by S. C. Cronwright-Schreiner). New York: Harper & Brothers, 1927.

Stories, Dreams and Allegories. New York: Frederick A. Stokes Co., 1923.

The Story of An African Farm (with an introduction by S. C. Cronwright-Schreiner). Boston: Little, Brown, and Co., 1924.

Thoughts on South Africa. New York: Frederick A. Stokes Co., 1923.

Trooper Peter Halket of Mashonaland. Boston: Roberts Brothers, 1897.

Woman and Labor. New York: Frederick A. Stokes Co., 1911. 8th ed.

The Story of An African Farm

*A*fter struggling to see the unseeable, growing drunk with the endeavor to span the infinite, and writhing before the inscrutable mystery, it is a renovating relief to turn to some simple, feelable, weighable substance; to something which has a smell and a color, which may be handled and turned over this way and that. Whether there be or be not a hereafter, whether there be any use in calling aloud to the Unseen Power, whether there be an Unseen Power to call to, whatever be the true nature of the *I* who call and of the objects around me, whatever be our meaning, our internal essence, our cause (and in a certain order of minds death and the agony of loss inevitably awaken the wild desire, at other times smothered, to look into these things), whatever be the nature of that which lies beyond the unbroken wall which the limits of the human intellect build up on every hand, this thing is certain—a knife will cut wood, and one cogged wheel will turn another. This is sure.   113–114*

The road to honor is paved with thorns; but on the path to truth, at every step you set your foot down on your own heart. 167

Now we have no God. We have had two: the old God that our fathers handed down to us, that we hated, and never liked; the new one that we made for ourselves, that we loved; but now he has flitted away from us, and we see what he has made of—the

---

*Numbers refer to original text pages

3

shadow of our highest ideal, crowned and throned. Now we have no God.

"The fool hath said in his heart, There is no God." It may be so. Most things said or written have been the work of fools.

This thing is certain—he is a fool who says, "No man hath said in his heart, There is no God."

It has been said many thousand times in hearts with profound bitterness of earnest faith.

We do not cry and weep; we sit down with cold eyes and look at the world. We are not miserable. Why should we be? We eat and drink, and sleep all night; but the dead are not colder.

And, we say it slowly, but without sighing, "Yes, we see it now: there is no God."

And we add, growing a little colder yet, "There is no justice. The ox dies in the yoke, beneath its master's whip; it turns its anguish-filled eyes on the sunlight, but there is no sign of recompense to be made it. The black man is shot like a dog, and it goes well with the shooter. The innocent are accused, and the accuser triumphs. If you will take the trouble to scratch the surface anywhere, you will see under the skin a sentient being writhing in impotent anguish."

And, we say further, and our heart is as the heart of the dead for coldness, "There is no order: all things are driven about by a blind chance."

What a soul drinks in with its mother's milk will not leave it in a day. From our earliest hour we have been taught that the thought of the heart, the shaping of the rain-cloud, the amount of wool that grows on a sheep's back, the length of a draught, and the growing of the corn, depend on nothing that moves immutable, at the heart of all things; but on the changeable will of a changeable being, whom our prayers can alter. To us, from the beginning, Nature has been but a poor plastic thing, to be toyed with this way or that, as man happens to please his deity or not;

to go to church or not; to say his prayers right or not; to travel on a Sunday or not. Was it possible for us in an instant to see Nature as she is—the flowing vestment of an unchanging reality? When a soul breaks free from the arms of a superstition, bits of the claws and talons break themselves off in him. It is not the work of a day to squeeze them out.

And so, for us, the human-like driver and guide being gone, all existence, as we look out at it with our chilled, wondering eyes, is an aimless rise and swell of shifting waters. In all that weltering chaos we can see no spot so large as a man's hand on which we may plant our foot.

Whether a man believes in a human-like God or no is a small thing. Whether he looks into the mental and physical world and sees no relation between cause and effect, no order, but a blind chance sporting, this is the mightiest fact that can be recorded in any spiritual existence. It were almost a mercy to cut his throat, if indeed he does not do it for himself.

We, however, do not cut our throats. To do so would imply some desire and feeling, and we have no desire and no feeling; we are only cold. We do not wish to live, and we do not wish to die. One day a snake curls itself round the waist of a Kaffir woman. We take it in our hand, swing it round and round, and fling it on the ground—dead. Everyone looks at us with eyes of admiration. We almost laugh. Is it wonderful to risk that for which we care nothing?

In truth, nothing matters. This dirty little world full of confusion, and the blue rag, stretched overhead for a sky, is so low we could touch it with our hand.   168–170

We marvel; not perceiving that what a man expends in prayer and ecstasy he cannot have over for acquiring knowledge. You never shed a tear or create a beautiful image, or quiver with emotion, but you pay for it at the practical, calculating end of your nature.

You have just so much force: when the one channel runs over the other runs dry.   171

This thing we call existence; is it not a something which has its roots far down below in the dark, and its branches stretching out into the immensity above, which we among the branches cannot see? Not a chance jumble; a living thing, a *One*. The thought gives us intense satisfaction, we cannot tell why.

And so, it comes to pass in time, that the earth ceases for us to be a weltering chaos. We walk in the great hall of life, looking up and round reverentially. Nothing is despicable—all is meaningful; nothing is small—all is part of a whole, whose beginning and end we know not. The life that throbs in us is a pulsation from it; too mighty for our comprehension, not too small.

And so, it comes to pass at last, that whereas the sky was at first a small blue rag stretched out over us, and so low that our hands might touch it, pressing down on us, it raises itself into an immeasurable blue arch over our heads, and we begin to live again.   174-175

It must be very nice to believe in the Devil, . . .; I wish I did. If it would be of any use I would pray three hours night and morning on my bare knees, "God, let me believe in Satan." He is so useful to those people who do. They may be as selfish and as sensual as they please, and, between God's will and the Devil's action, always have some one to throw their sin on. But we, wretched unbelievers, we bear our own burdens; we must say, "I, myself did it, *I*. Not God, not Satan; I myself!" That is the sting that strikes deep.   252-253

When my own life feels small, and I am oppressed with it, I like to crush together, and see it in a picture, in an instant, a multitude of disconnected unlike phases of human life—a mediaeval monk

with his string of beads pacing the quiet orchard, and looking up
from the grass at his feet to the heavy fruit-trees; little Malay boys
playing naked on a shining sea-beach; a Hindoo philosopher
alone under his banyan tree, thinking, thinking, thinking, so that
in the thought of God he may lose himself; a troop of Bacchanali-
ans dressed in white, with crowns of vine-leaves, dancing along
the Roman streets; a martyr on the night of his death looking
through the narrow window to the sky, and feeling that already
he has the wings that shall bear him up . . .; an Epicurean dis-
coursing at a Roman bath to a knot of his disciples on the nature
of happiness; a Kaffir witch-doctor seeking for herbs by moonlight, while from the huts on the hill-side come the sound of dogs
barking, and the voices of women and children; a mother giving
bread and milk to her children in little wooden basins and singing
the evening song. I like to see it all; I feel it run through me—
that life belongs to me; it makes my little life larger; it breaks
down the narrow walls that shut me in.

. . . . I wish I could help you; I wish I could make you see that
you must decide what you will be and do. It does not matter what
you choose—be a farmer, business-man, artist, what you will—
but know your aim, and live for that one thing. We have only one
life. The secret of success is concentration; wherever there has
been a great life, or a great work, that has gone before. Taste
everything a little, look at everything a little; but live for one
thing. Anything is possible to a man who knows his end and
moves straight for it, and for it alone.   259–260

"Do you ever pray?". . .
    "No."
    "I never do; but I might when I look up there. I will tell
you . . . where I could pray. If there were a wall of rock on the
edge of a world, and one rock stretched out far, far into space,
and I stood alone upon it, alone, with stars above me, and stars

below me—I would not say anything; but the feeling would be prayer." 264

There are as many kinds of loves as there are flowers; everlastings that never wither; speedwells that wait for the wind to fan them out of life; blood-red mountain-lilies that pour their voluptuous sweetness out for one day, and lie in the dust at night. There is no flower has the charm of all—the speedwell's purity, the ever-lasting's strength, the mountain-lily's warmth; but who knows whether there is no love that holds all—friendship, passion, worship?

Such a love . . . will fall on the surface of strong, cold, selfish life as the sunlight falls on a torpid winter world; there, where the trees are bare, and the ground frozen, till it rings to the step like iron, and the water is solid, and the air is sharp as a two-edged knife, that cuts the unwary. But, when its sun shines on it, through its whole dead crust a throbbing yearning wakes: the trees feel him, and every knot and bud swell, aching to open to him. The brown seeds, who have slept deep under the ground, feel him, and he gives them strength, till they break through the frozen earth, and lift two tiny, trembling green hands in love to him. And he touches the water, till down to its depths it feels him and melts, and it flows, and the things, strange sweet things that were locked up in it, it sings as it runs, for love of him. Each plant tries to bear at least one fragrant little flower for him; and the world that was dead lives, and the heart that was dead and self-centered throbs, with an upward, outward yearning, and it has become that which it seemed impossible ever to become. 277-278

You may work a man's body so that his soul dies. Work is good. I have worked at the old farm from the sun's rising till its setting, but I have had time to think, and time to feel. You may work a man so that all but the animal in him is gone; and that grows stronger with physical labor. You may work a man till he is a devil. I know it, because I have felt it. You will never understand the change that came over me. No one but I will ever know how great it was. But I was never miserable; when I could keep my oxen from sticking fast, and when I could find a place to lie down in, I had all I wanted. After I had driven eight months a rainy season came. For eighteen hours out of the twenty-four we worked in the wet. The mud went up to the axles sometimes, and we had to dig the wheels out, and we never went far in a day. My master swore at me more than ever, but when he had done he always offered me his brandy-flask. When I first came he had offered it me, and I had always refused; but now I drank as my oxen did when I gave them water—without thinking.   313

"But the old love life."...

   "They love life, they do not want to die ...; but what of that? They have had their time. They knew that a man's life is three-score years and ten; they should have made their plans accordingly! But the young ..., the young cut down cruelly, when they have not seen, when they have not known—when they have not found—it is for them that the bells weep blood. I heard in the ringing it was an old man. When the old die—Listen to the bell! it is laughing—'It is right, it is right: he has had his time.' They cannot ring so for the young."   342

I see the vision of a poor weak soul striving after good. It was not cut short; and in the end it learned, through tears and much pain, that holiness is an infinite compassion for others; that greatness is to take the common things of life, and walk truly among them. That ... happiness is a great love and much serving.   347

And, at last, as he walked there with his bent head, his soul passed down the steps of contemplation into that vast land where there is always peace; that land where the soul, gazing long, loses all consciousness of its little self, and almost feels its hand on the old mystery of Universal Unity that surrounds it. "No death, no death," he muttered; "there is that which never dies—which abides. It is but the individual that perishes, the whole remains. It is the organism that vanishes, the atoms are there. It is but the man that dies, the Universal Whole of which he is part reworks him into its inmost self. Ah, what matter that man's day be short! —that the sunrise sees him, and the sunset sees his grave; that of which he is but the breath has breathed him forth and drawn him back again. That abides—we abide."

For the little soul that cries aloud for continued personal existence for itself and its beloved, there is no help. For the soul which knows itself no more as a unit, but as a part of the Universal Unity of which the Beloved also is a part; which feels within itself the throb of the Universal Life; for that soul there is no death.

"Let us die, beloved, you and I, that we may pass on forever through the Universal Life!"   360–361

Go out if you will, and walk alone on the hillside in the evening, but if your favorite child lies ill at home, or your lover comes to-morrow, or at your heart there lies a scheme for the holding of wealth, then you will return as you went out; you will have seen nothing. For Nature, ever, like the old Hebrew God, cries out, "Thou shalt have no other gods before me." Only then, when there comes a pause, a blank in your life, when the old idol is broken, when the old hope is dead, when the old desire is crushed, then the Divine compensation of Nature is made manifest. She shows herself to you. So near she draws you, that the blood seems to flow from her to you, through a still uncut cord: you feel the throb of her life.

When that day comes, that you sit down broken, without one human creature to whom you cling, with your loves the dead and the living-dead; when the very thirst for knowledge through long-continued thwarting has grown dull; when in the present there is no craving, and in the future no hope, then, oh, with a beneficent tenderness, Nature enfolds you.   372

Well to die then; for, if you live, so surely as the years come, so surely as the spring succeeds the winter, so surely will passions arise. They will creep back, one by one, into the bosom that has cast them forth, and fasten there again, and peace will go. Desire, ambition, and the fierce agonizing flood of love for the living— they will spring again. Then Nature will draw down her veil: with all your longing you shall not be able to raise one corner; you cannot bring back those peaceful days. Well to die then!   372– 373

Ah, to live on so, year after year, how well! Always in the present, letting each day glide, bringing its own labor, and its own beauty, the gradual lighting up of the hills, night and the stars, firelight and the coals! To live on so, calmly, far from the paths of men; and to look at the lives of clouds and insects; to look deep into the heart of flowers, and see how lovingly the pistil and the stamens nestle there together; and to see in the thorn-pods how the little seeds suck their life through the delicate curled-up string, and how the little embryo sleeps inside! Well, how well, to sit so on one side, taking no part in the world's life; but when great men blossom into books, looking into those flowers also, to see how the world of men too opens beautifully, leaf after leaf. Ah! life is delicious; well to live long, and see the darkness breaking, and the day coming! The day when soul shall not thrust back soul that would come to it; when men shall not be driven to seek solitude, because of the crying-out of their hearts for love and sympathy. Well to live long and see the new time breaking. Well to live long; life is sweet, sweet, sweet!   373–374

Thoughts on South Africa

$\mathcal{T}$he incapacity of peoples to pass judgments on the surroundings from which they have never been separated is familiar to every traveller. The inhabitant of one of the rarest and fairest towns in the colonies or on earth does not boast to you of his oaks and grapes, or ask you what you think of his mountain, or explain to you the marvellous mixture of races in his streets; but he is anxious to know what you think of his docks and small public buildings. He has not the emotional detachment necessary for the forming of a large critical judgment. A certain distance is necessary to the seeing of great wholes clearly. It is not by any chance that the most scientific exposition of American Democracy is the work of a Frenchman, that the best history of the French Revolution is by an Englishman, or that the finest history of English literature is the work of a Frenchman. Distance is essential for a keen, salient survey, which shall take in large outlines and mark prominent characteristics. 28

There is a certain knowledge of land which is only to be gained by one born in it, or brought into long-continued, close, personal contact with it, and which in its perfection is perhaps never obtained by any man with regard to a country which he has not inhabited before he was thirty. It is the subjective emotional sympathy with its nature, and the comprehension not merely of the vices and virtues of its people, but of the how and why of their existence, which is possible to a man only with regard to a country that is more or less his own. The stranger sees the barren

15

scene, but of the emotion which that barren mountain is capable of awakening in the man who lives under its shadow he knows nothing. He marks the curious custom, but of the social condition which originated it, and the passions concerned in its maintenance, he understands absolutely nothing.   29

Those motionless hills; the very knotted Karoo stem at your hand, for how many generations have the leaves sprouted and fallen from its gnarled stalk? The Bushman and the wild buck have crept over the scene; they have gone, and the Englishman with his horse and gun have come; but the plain lies with its sharp stones turned to the sky unchanged through the centuries. Those two stones standing loosely one upon another have stood so for thousands of years, because there was no hand to sever them.

It is not fear one feels, with that clear, blue sky above one; that which creeps over one is not dread. It was amid such scenes as these, amid such motionless, immeasurable silences, that the Oriental mind first framed its noblest conception of the unknown, the "I am that I am" of the Hebrew.   41

For not only is South Africa peopled everywhere by a mixture of races overlying and underlying each other in confused layers; but these mixtures of peoples are redivided into political states whose boundaries, except in the case of a few of the necessarily ephemeral native states, have no relation to the racial divisions of the people beneath them, but are purely the result of more or less political combination and therefore have in them, at core, nothing of the true nature of national divisions.

This matter lies so deeply at the heart of the South African, and has so much to do with our complicated problem, that it will be well to look at it more closely.

A nation, like an individual, is a combination of units; in the nation the units are persons; in the individual body they are cells.

The single cell, alone and uncombined, is capable only of the simplest forms of development; the solitary amoeboid germ can undergo no high development, as it floats unconnected in the water or air; it is only when cells are combined in close and vital union with others, and there is interaction, that high development is possible. The highly differentiated complex cells that go to form a human eye or brain are possible only as parts of a larger interacting organism, a long-continued and close interaction between millions of cells, and could come into being in no other way.

Yet more is the analogous fact true with regard to human beings. Alone and divided from his fellows, the individual man is capable of only the very lowest form of development. The accounts of persons who have been lost in infancy and grown up alone, apart from any organization or interaction with their fellows, show in the extremest form how very low is the natural condition of the human amoeboid. Speechless, knowledgeless, its very hands incapable of performing the simplest operation which the veriest child in the lowest organized society learns to perform (as we imagine intuitively), such an individuality impresses on us, in its extremest form, a lesson which all human history teaches us in other shapes.

Great men, great actions, great arts, great developments, are impossible without those closely united, interacting organic combinations of men which we call nations, using that word in its largest sense, and to include all organized, centralized, interacting masses of humans and to exclude such as are inorganic and only united in name or by force. The organically united nation is the only known matrix in which the human being can attain to full development. A Plato, an Aristotle, a Shakespeare, a Michael Angelo, implying as much the existence of a Greece, an England, or an Italy, are as impossible without them as an eye or brain imply and would be impossible without a whole human organism. They are the efflorescence of the nations.   52–54

For there is a sense in which all South Africans are one. It is not only that all men born in South Africa, from the Zambesi to the Cape, are bound by the associations of their early years to the same vast, untamed nature; it is not only that South Africa itself, situated at the extremity of the continent, shut off by vast seas and impassable forests from the rest of the world, forces upon its inhabitants a certain union, like that of a crew who, in the same ship, set out on an interminable voyage together; there is a subtle but a very real bond, which unites all South Africans, and differentiates us from all other peoples in the world. *This bond is our mixture of races itself.* It is this which divides South Africans from all other peoples in the world, and makes us one. From Zambesi to the sea the same mixture exists, in slightly varying form, and the same problem is found. Wherever a Dutchman, an Englishman, a Jew, and a native are superimposed, there is that common South African condition through which no dividing line can be drawn. The only form of organization which can be healthily or naturally assumed by us is one which takes cognizance of this universal condition. Great and seemingly insuperable as are for the moment the difficulties which lie in our path on the way to a great, common, national unity, no man can study South Africa without feeling that, in this form, and this alone, is national life and organization attainable by South Africa. Difficult as it may be, it is at once simpler and easier than the consolidation of any separate part. It is the one form of crystallization open to us, the one shape we shall assume.   60–61

How, of our divided peoples, can a great, healthy, harmonious and desirable nation be formed?

This is the final problem of South Africa. If we cannot solve it, our fate is sealed. If South Africa is unable so to co-ordinate, and, where she cannot blend, so to harmonize her differing peoples, that if in years to come a foreign foe should land upon her shores, and but six men were left to defend her, two English, two Dutch, two of native extraction: if those six men would not stand shoulder to shoulder, fighting for a land that was their own, in which each felt, widely as he might otherwise be separated from his fellows, that he had a stake,—then the fate of South Africa is sealed; the handwriting has already appeared on the wall against us; we must take for ever a last place among the nations; however large, rich, populous we may become, we shall never be able to look free, united peoples in the face. In past ages empires have existed which were founded on racial hatred and force. Of this type were the great states of antiquity—Egypt, Assyria, Rome, and Greece. They passed away; but for a time they were able to maintain themselves against states of like construction with themselves, only falling when they came into contact with freer and more united peoples. 63

Taken as a whole, so vast, so complex, and so beset with difficulty is our South African problem, that it may be truly said that no European nation has had during the last eight hundred years to face anything approaching it in complexity and difficulty. To find any analogy to it we must go back as far as the England of Alfred, when divided Saxons and invading Danes were the elements out of which organic unity had to be constructed. But there are elements in our problem which no European nation has ever had to face, and which no migrating part of a European race has ever had to deal with, in exactly the same form in which they met us. Our race question is complicated by a question of colour, which presents itself to us in a form more virulent and intense than that in which it has met any modern people. America and India have nothing analogous to it; and it has to be faced in an age which does not allow of the old methods in dealing with alien and so-called inferior peoples. In South Africa the nineteenth century is brought face to face with a prehistoric world.   64

The Huguenot ancestor of the Boer left a country in which not only the Government, but the body of his fellows were at deadly variance with him; in which his religion was an exotic and his mental attitude alien from that of the main body of the people.

To these men, when they shook off the dust of their feet against her, France became the visible embodiment of the powers of evil; her rule was the rule of Agag, whom the Lord should yet hew in pieces; her people were the children of Satan, given over to believe a lie, and her fields were the plains of Sodom and Gomorrah, on which in judgment the Almighty would yet rain down fire and brimstone; a righteous Lot fled from them in horror with all that he had. To these homeless fugitives the Europe that they had left was as the "house of bondage." The ships which bore them to South Africa were the Ark of the Covenant of the Lord their God, in which He bore His chosen to the Land of His Promise. As the Huguenot paced the deck of his ship and saw the strange stars of the Southern Hemisphere come out above him, like Abraham of old he read in them the promise of his covenant-keeping God:—"To thee and thy seed shall the land be given and they shall inherit it. Look up and see the stars of heaven if thou canst count them: so shall thy seed be for multitude; like sand, like fine sand on the seashore. And when thou comest to the land that I shall give thee, thou shalt drive out the heathen from before thee."   82–83

Deep in the hearts of every old veld-schoen-wearing Boer that you may meet, side by side with an almost religious indifference to other lands and peoples, lies this deep, mystical and impersonal affection for South Africa. Not for the land, as inhabited by human beings, and formed into social and political organizations of which he is a part; not for the land, regarded as a social and political entity alone, is it that he feels affection. It is for the actual physical country, with its plains, rocks and skies, that his love and veneration are poured out (absolutely incomprehensible as this may appear to the money-making nineteenth-century Englishman). The primitive Boer believes he possesses this land by a right wholly distinct from that of the aborigines whom he dispossesses, or the Englishmen who followed him; a right with which no claim of theirs can ever conflict. His feeling for South Africa is not in any way analogous to the feeling of the Johannesburg digger or speculator for the land in which he has "made his pile," nor even to that of the ordinary colonist for the territory in which his habitation lies; nor is it quite of the same nature as the passion of the old-world Swiss for his mountains, nor of the Norwegian for his fjords. Its only true counterpart is to be found in the attitude of the Jew towards Palestine—"When I forget thee, O Jerusalem!" His feeling towards it is a faith, not a calculation. It is as useless to attempt to influence the Boer by showing him that he will derive material advantage by giving up the rule of his land to others, as it is to try and persuade an ardent lover that he gains by sharing his mistress with one who will contribute to her support. His feeling for South Africa is not primarily based on utilitarian calculations or considerations of the material advantages to accrue to him from its possession; it is the one vein of idealism and romance underlying his seemingly prosaic and leaden existence. Touch the Boer on the side of South Africa, and at once, for the moment, he is hero and saint—his feeling for it a religion.   84–85

A white-headed Basuto man of seventy came to us once with a cow and a calf, the most prized of his earthly possessions, offering to give both if he could be taught to read, and went away in tears when told it was impossible. "Ah! it is because you do not wish me to be wise like the white man," he murmured bitterly.   111

Each Bantu tribe holds its land in common; re-apportioning it as the increase or diminution of its numbers may require. The doctrine that land can become the private property of one is a doctrine morally repugnant to the Bantu. The idea which to-day is beginning to haunt Europe, that, as the one possible salve for our social wounds and diseases, it might be well if the land should become again the property of the nation at large, is no ideal to the Bantu, but a realistic actuality. He finds it difficult, if not impossible, to reconcile his sense of justice with any other form of tenure. And it is only painfully and slowly (and perhaps never quite successfully!) that under the pressure of autocratic European rule he is brought to allow that absolute, individual property in land may be consistent with right. It may be remarked in passing that if it be desired to deal justly with the South African native, it is as necessary to grasp this mental attitude of his with regard to the possession of land as in dealing with the Boer it is necessary never to forget his theocratic conception of his claim on South Africa, and his passionate affection for it.   113

The little Bushman when we pressed him hard could creep away among his stones, and die; leaving nothing behind him but his little arrowheads beside the fountains and his bits of pictures on the rocks and stones, to show how he too was once on the path to become human. And our little Tottie could laugh and dodge and play at working, till he also has vanished, leaving only a few Half-caste descendants, soon to fade away after him. And our Bantu, still with us and increasing in numbers, sets his broad back persistently against compulsion to perform unremunerated labour, his strong social and tribal feeling making him hard to crush. In truth our early fellow countrymen were and are as little fitted to play the part of the dumb instruments of labour as the South African Boer or the South African Englishman of to-day.

That little door, which nature always leaves ajar that the meanest of her creatures who will may go out by it, and escape—where the voice of the oppressor is heard no more—that little door we all of us know how to enter if need be, rather than lay aside the "I will" that makes the man. If we know nothing else, at least we all of us know how to die. 115–116

It is sometimes thrown into the teeth of the Boer, as an accusation which sets him on a completely lower platform than that on which his English fellow-citizen stands, that his fathers were slave-owners. That this should be so is, indeed, remarkable; not only when we reflect that most of those ships which brought the first slaves to South Africa were the property of Englishmen and manned and officered by English seamen; but when we further reflect that, if the houses and avenues of the Cape Peninsula are often the work of slaves, the yet fairer homes and the easeful leisure of certain cultured English men and women at the present day are the result of their fathers' traffic in black flesh. And it is yet more remarkable that the fact of a slave-owning ancestry should ever be thrown in the face of the Boer when we reflect that it is not forty years since the leading branch of the Anglo-Saxon people found no other means of removing the institution from among themselves than by rending their national life well-nigh to fragments.

Slavery is, in truth, a condition so common in the very early stages of social growth, and when it occurs in those stages is generally so comparatively innoxious that it may almost be regarded as a natural if not quite healthy concomitant of early social development. When the primitive master and his slave live in like huts, share like food, and are engaged in like occupations, slavery is slavery in nothing but name. It is exactly in proportion as a

society has attained to a high intellectual and material development that the institution exhibits its most malignant features;
causing an arrest of both moral and material progress in any
highly cultured and civilized society in the midst of which it is
found.

Slavery may, perhaps, be best compared to the infantile disease
of measles; a complaint which so commonly attacks the young of
humanity in their infancy, and when gone through at that period
leaves behind it so few fatal marks; but which when it abnormally
attacks the fully developed adult becomes one of the most virulent and toxic of diseases, often permanently poisoning the constitution where it does not end in death.   116–117

If it be asked, "Was slavery, as carried out at the Cape, of a more
or less vindictive nature than as carried on among other civilized
nations?" the reply can only be that slavery among civilized folk
is a disease so monotonous in its symptoms that whether we study
its story as inlaid on the mud tablets of ruined Chaldean cities,
or as described in Greek or Roman literature, or view its image
in such stone picture as that which Sennacherib, King of Assyria,
caused to be made (and which to-day hangs on the walls of the
British Museum for him who wills to see); or whether, on the
other hand, we examine it as described in the nineteenth-century
novel, or sit in the evening beside the old Boer grandmother, as,
with her feet on her stove, she describes the remembrance of her
far-off youth—the story is one, and its details monotonously un-
varying.

Old white men and women are still living in South Africa who
can remember how, in their early days, they saw men with guns
out in the beautiful woods at Newlands hunting runaway slaves.
They can tell you what a mistress once did when a slave became
pregnant by her master; and there are stories about hot ovens—
such stories as the story of Dirk, whose master seduced his wife,

and Dirk bitterly resented it. "And one day," says the narrator, "we children saw Dirk taken across the yard to the wine house; we heard he was to be flogged. For some days after we fancied we heard noises in the cellar. One night, in the moonlight, we heard something, and got up and looked out; and we saw something slipped across the yard by three men. We children dared say nothing, because my grandfather never let anyone remark about the slaves; but we were sure it was Dirk's body." There is nothing new in these stories; they are as old as the times of the Romans and Chaldeans, and older than the ruin of Nineveh which they preceded. They would be echoed by the walls of half the out-buildings still standing in Jamaica and Cuba, had they the power of speech. To pretend we have never heard them before is hypocrisy; to be surprised at them is folly; to imply that they are peculiar to South Africa and the outcome of the abnormal structure of the Boer soul is a lie.

Old black men and women are still living in South Africa who remember how, as little children, they were playing on a beach in a hot land, where there were tall, straight trees that do not grow in South Africa, and how white men came and took them away. They remember the names of some of their playmates; and the "yellow food" that they used to eat, they say it does not grow here. If you look at their backs, from their necks to below their thighs they have white stripes which have been there for sixty or seventy years, and with which they will go to their graves. Neither in this is there anything peculiarly South African.   118–119

There are times to-day, riding across the plains in the direction of Hottentots Holland, when the vision of these creatures creeping across the veld in search of freedom comes suddenly to one; and a curious feeling rises. We are not in that band that rides booted and spurred across the plain, looking out to right and left and talking loud. We are in the little group cowering behind the milk bushes; we are looking out with furtive, bloodshot eyes, to see how the masters ride! We—we—are there;—we are no more conscious of our identity with the dominant race. Over a million years of diverse evolution white man clasps dark again—and we are one, as we cower behind the bushes; the black and the white.

But slavery in South Africa, as elsewhere, did not always show its misshapen and deformed side; there were cases in which as men grew up they learnt to feel gently to the hands that had tended them in early infancy, and showed kindness; and kindness begat gratitude, and gratitude begat love—and the circle of human beatitude was complete. In certain rare instances the words master and slave came to mean not user and used, but giver and lover, and human nature was justified in the lowest of her kinships.   120

The causes and evils of slavery are not to be studied in South Africa or America, but among the shadows within our own hearts. And this much-talked-of slavery in South Africa was but what you and I, and the man over the way would have made it had we lived in South Africa two hundred years ago.

Slavery in its legal form was extinguished at the Cape about the year 1834. The English Government, who had at that time taken over the Colony, purchased and liberated all the slaves at the cost of £1,247,000. Official slavery passed away; but it left, as always, its indelible marks on the dominant race who had suffered from it. . . .

Slavery bequeathed to the Boer, and to South Africa mainly through him, its large Half-caste population: a population which constitutes at once the most painful, and most complex, and—if any social problem were insoluble in the presence of human energy and sympathy, we might add—the most insoluble portion of our South African national problem.

The bulk of that Half-caste population which to-day fills our

Western towns and throngs upon our Western farms, and which is found scattered over the whole of South Africa, arose originally and mainly as the result of sexual intercourse between the Boer and his imported slaves; and also with such aboriginal Hottentots or Bushmen, as he obtained possession of. 121–122

We are each of us our own ideal. The black may envy the white his power or his knowledge, but he admires himself most. "You say the devil is black! But I picture him a white man with blue eyes and yellow hair," said to us a Bantu once. "I have a great sorrow," said an intelligent native preacher. "I know that the Lord Jesus Christ was a white man, yet I could not pray to Him and love Him as I do if I did not picture Him as black and with wool like myself." 127

Of that divine contentment with his own inalienable personality which lies at the root of all the heroic and half the social virtues, the Half-caste can know little. If it were possible for him with red-hot pincers to draw out every ounce of flesh that was black man's, and leave only the white, in most cases he would do it. That race which would accept him he despises; and the race he aspires to refuses him. 127

In those countries in which the wild elephant is found, it is well known that when, as frequently happens, an individual is expelled from the herd, and compelled to wander alone, his nature frequently undergoes a change. Originally of the same character as the rest of the group, the mild and retiring nature of the social elephant leaves him. He not only attacks man and beast without provocation, but in his spleen rends branches from the trees, and ploughs up the earth with his tusks. He is then known as the rogue elephant, and, hated and feared by man and beast, if he does not in a few years die, worn out with his own ill temper, he is killed by the creatures he attacks.   132

There were cases in which the ordinary Half-caste did not marry into the dark race, but again into the white, their descendants becoming ultimately almost purely white. There were also cases, though they were rare, in which love and genuine respect found the gulf which divides race from race not wide enough to prevent their crossing, and in which white men took as their lawful wives women of dark race. The offspring of these lawful marriages naturally remarried into the white race; and so it comes to pass to-day that there are certain white men and women, both Dutch and English, often of the greatest natural intelligence, and some-times of great culture, wealth, and physical beauty, who have in their veins this remote trace of non-European blood.

These folks are often essentially and practically entirely Aryan; the remote strain of dark blood during seven or eight generations of white inbreeding being practically so eliminated that it is no more present than a nightmare of ten years ago is present within my brains to-day; and no more manifest than in the bull-dog who may win first prize at a show is manifested the fact that, eight generations before, his ancestral tables show a strain of spaniel blood. Nevertheless, in South Africa, difficult as it may appear for those who have only lived in Europe and who have never mingled with persons of mixed race to conceive it, the position of such individuals is often one of pain and difficulty, and the cause of as acute suffering as any which human creatures are called on to go through. Over the heads of such men and women in South Africa dangles a sword, which a twirl from the hand of the most brutal and ignorant passer-by may at any moment send to their hearts. And, as the low-bred cur, safe behind a grating, may bark with safety at the noblest mastiff passing by, so the meanest and most ill-descended beings, sheltered behind the consciousness of an unmixed Aryan pedigree, may taunt with their descent men and women the latchet of whose shoes they may not be worthy to unloose.

The true anguish of the position lies in the fact that so strong is the Aryan prejudice against colour, that it affects the individuals themselves; a taunt with regard to dark ancestry is always felt by the person against whom it is directed as the most cruel and unanswerable of blows, the extent of their silent suffering being measured by the fact that as a rule no reply is ever attempted, and that by their nearest friends it may not be referred to. It may be doubted whether, even within the families themselves which are so situated, the fact of such descent is ever openly discussed, as men in a chamber where one is dying seldom use the word death —the thing itself is too near.   142–143

As the modern gardener who has a rare and highly developed double rose, a Maréchal Neil or Cloth of Gold, if he wish it to be of exceptional beauty and sturdy growth, does not graft it on the stalk of another rare highly developed rose, but on a root of the old single wild rose, from which all roses descended, so it may be that the mingling with a more primitive type, under certain conditions, may fasten the roots of a race on earth: and that even the despised African may have some other mission towards humanity, as a whole, than the mere hewing of its wood and drawing of its water, even the building up of the rough physical basis of its life—allowing all this as possible, it is yet difficult to conceive the condition under which the action which originates a cross between the dark and light races in South Africa to-day shall not be anti-social, and its results almost unmitigatedly evil, whether the offspring be rendered anti-social by inheritance or circumstances; or, whether, rising in the scale of being, they attain to the highest point of development, and pay merely in unmerited suffering for the action of others.   144–145

What the Black man is we know, what the White man is we know: what the ultimate result of this commingling will be no man to-day knows.   145

It is easy for *us* to feel tender over his little paintings when suddenly we come across them among the rocks; the artist in us recognizes across the chasm of a million centuries of development its little kinsman. Something in us nods back to him across the years:—"I know why you did that, little brother: I do it too —another way, pen or pencil or stone, it doesn't matter which. You call it an ox: I call it truth. We both paint what we see, the likest we can! They never know why we do it. Did you look at your oxen and your zebras and your ostriches, and feel that you must and you must, till you painted or etched them? Take my hand, brother manikin!"

Ring round head, ears on pedestals, his very vital organs differing from the rest of his race—yet, as one sits under the shelving rocks at the top of some African mountain, the wall behind one covered with his crude little pictures, the pigments of which are hardly faded through the long ages of exposure, and, as one looks out over the great shimmering expanse of mountain and valleys beneath, one feels that that spirit which is spread abroad over existence concentrated itself in those little folk who climbed among the rocks; and that that which built the Parthenon and raised St. Peter's, and carved the statues of Michael Angelo in the Medici Chapel, and which moves in every great work of man, moved here also. That that Spirit of Life which, incarnate in humanity, seeks to recreate existence as it beholds it, and which we call art, worked through that small monkey hand too! And that shelving cave on the African mountain becomes for us a temple, in which first the hand of humanity raised itself quiveringly in the worship of the true and of the beautiful.

And when in the valley below we come suddenly across a little arrow-head beside some old drinking-fountain, or find a spot where his flints and empty mussel-shells lie thick among the soil on the bank of a sloot where for this many hundred years now no mussels have been, a curious thrill of interest comes to us: we feel as would an adult who in middle life should come suddenly across the shoes and toys he had used in earliest childhood, carefully laid up together.

And we sit down and dig out the shells and flints with our fingers and the warm afternoon sunshine shimmers over us, as it did over some old first mother of humanity when she sat there cracking shells. And we touch with our hands the old race days, that at other times are hardly realizable by us.   153–154

St. Francis of Assisi preached to the little fishes: we eat them. But the man who eats fish can hardly be blamed, seeing that the eating of fishes is all but universal among the human race!—if only he does not pretend that while he eats he preaches to them!
    155

We, as civilized men, must recognize that the extinction of a species of beast, and yet more a species of man, is an order of Vandalism compared with which the destruction of Greek marbles by barbarians, or of classical manuscripts by the Christians, were trifles; for it is within the range of a remote possibility that again among mankind some race may arise which shall produce such statues as those of Phidias, or that the human brain may yet again blossom forth into the wisdom and beauty incarnate in the burnt books; but a race of living things, once destroyed, is gone for ever—it reappears on earth no more. We are conscious that we are murdering the heritage of unborn generations; yet we take no step to stay the destruction.   156

Nor is it probable that South Africa has lost by this return to a condition of almost primitive simplicity on the part of a section of her white inhabitants. As it is necessary that the artist or thinker who is to instruct mankind should not live too far from the unmodified life of nature, if he is to accomplish work that shall have in it the deathless elements of truth and virility; so it seems to be a law of existence that the most dominant and powerful races, if they desire to keep their virility, cannot remove themselves too far and too long from the primitive conditions of life. As the great individual is seldom found more than three generations removed from ancestors who wrought with their hands and lived in the open air, so the most powerful races seldom survive more than a few centuries of the enervation of an artificial life. As the physical body becomes toneless and weakened, so also the intellectual life grows thin; and it is as necessary for the nation, as for the individual who would recuperate, to return again and again, and, lying flat on the bosom of our common mother, to suck direct from the breast of nature the milk of life, which, drawn through long artificial channels, tends to become thin and ceases to nourish. Most great conquering peoples have been within hail of the nomads' encampment; and all great nations at the time when they have attained their greatness were largely agricultural or pastoral. The city kills.   160–161

And Death comes here. The old grandmother goes from her chair in the corner, and her favourite great-granddaughter inherits her stove; and the stories she used to tell of the old trekking days, and her faint childish memories of the Bovenland where she was born, become matters of tradition; and the little children are carried out often enough from the close rooms of the house, few surviving who were not very vigorous; and sometimes the great elbow-chair by the coffee-table itself becomes vacant, and the house-mother is carried away by an untoward child-birth, or a "hart-kwaal," [heart complaint] which is generally dropsy as well; her chair is not long left empty; but when the time comes for her husband to be carried out feet foremost, he often asks to be buried beside his first wife; and they sleep peacefully together under the piles of rough iron-stones behind the kopjes. 173

For, it may never be overlooked, that the intensity of human enjoyment does not vary as the intensity of the stimuli; but with the sensitiveness and power of response of the nerves concerned. As the youth obtains a more enjoyable exhilaration from his first glass of wine than the drunkard from his bottle, and the child from his sweetmeat than a gourmand from his dinner—so our African Boer, in common with all who lead a severely simple life, knows probably more of intense enjoyment than is compassed by a hundred men seeking always for new sensations and new stimulations. Is not the human soul a string which may soon be strung so tight and struck so often that it refuses to vibrate at all and ends by hanging limp; and the human life is a very small cup, where all beyond a certain amount poured into it runs to waste? 186–187

If the woman's movement of this country may be said to have its origin in any one class more than another, it is exactly among those women of the wealthier classes whom modern life has supplied with overwhelming liberality with all the material enjoyment and comfort which existence can yield; and who have no physical or sexual indulgence or material good to gain by change, but who have much to lose. It is these women, and not the overtasked labourer's wife with ten children to rear, feed, and labour for, it is these women above all who have started to their feet and are demanding the re-organization of their relations to life; and side by side with the factory girl and the ill-paid solitary spinster whom the struggle of life is driving to the wall, are found the millionaire's daughter and the countess, and the comfortably situated woman of the middle classes, for whom earth has left no material good unyielded. The Woman's Movement is essentially *not* a movement on the part of civilized women in search of greater enjoyment and physical ease.   205

Sitting beside a Bantu woman once as she knelt on the ground grinding her corn, we, anxious to arrive at her conception on religious matters, inquired of her whether she believed there was a God. She shook her head, and said that she did not; there might be a God, but if there were one, He was not good. When further we inquired why this was so, she replied that if God were good He would not have made women. There might be a God for the white woman, but there was certainly none for the black; and then she broke into a description of the condition of women in semi-barbarous societies, the force of which cannot be retained when translated from her picturesque and passionate language, but its substance was much as this:—"See there," pointing to two small girl children playing beside the huts, "they are happy now; they play all day; they play with their brothers; they think they are boys; it is good with them. Now, wait a little—when they are so high," raising her hand as high as she could reach kneeling, "it is still well with them. Then the breasts begin to grow; the people look, and say, she is beginning to be a woman; then they say, where are the cattle for her? Then a man comes, perhaps he is old; it does not matter—'Here, take her; give us the cattle.' She goes home with him. She plants the corn, she makes the hut; she makes his food for him. Soon the child begins to grow in her body; that is good. All day she works,"—putting her hand to her back—"her back aches; it doesn't matter. It is all right; she is glad she is going to have a child; the man will like her; he will not beat her. At night she cooks the food, she cleans round the hut, she has children, she grinds the corn! See there, all those baskets—

her hands made them full of corn! Then the wrinkles begin to come; see, her breasts get soft; she is old. Then the man comes home at night. 'Make haste, make haste,' he says, 'you do not grind the corn nicely.' She grinds it as she always ground it, but he beats her. 'Make haste, make haste! You are old—you are lazy! What is your face so ugly for?' She works; he beats her. See here" —pointing to her breast as though there were a mark on it—"he beats it with a whip: the blood comes out. Never mind. Take the child, put it at the breast, let it suck: the blood comes on its face. She wipes it off"—with an action of the hand as though she were wiping the blood off an imaginary child's face.—"Then he brings the young wife. The young wife is strong; her arms are still fat. She has still many children in her. The young wife says, 'Do this; do that.' The old wife must not speak. Then the breasts dry up —there is no milk in them. She works in the fields all day. She brings the wood home. 'Make haste! Make haste!' The old wife is done for! There—throw her away; she is good for nothing. Let her sit out there on the dung-heap! She is only a thing! The man can have as many wives as he likes. Yes, there is perhaps a God for the white woman; there is none for the black."   206–207

What is new is not that woman suffers or knows that she suffers. The woman of to-day probably suffers less than the women of any period, since that most primitive time when men and women both wandered free; the absolutely new thing is her conscious determination to modify her relation to life about her.

If, then, a Woman's Movement be not in its ultimate essence a sudden and insane desire on the part of woman for increased material enjoyment and physical ease, nor, on the other hand, the result of a sudden revelation to herself of her own sufferings, what in its ultimate essence is this movement?

Vast social phenomena, rising up in what appears to be obedience to an almost universal instinct, must be based on some equally comprehensive social condition, which acts everywhere as its cause; a cause which will not be less irresistibly operative because those who are acted upon by it have not always grasped it intellectually, nor are capable of reasoning on its nature. As those vast herds of antelope which at time sweep down across our South African plains from the north, bearing all before them, are propelled, not by any logical induction, the result of an intellectual process, but are driven onwards, whether they will or no, by the pressure of a stern fact which forces itself painfully on the consciousness of each isolated individual in the herd—the fact, that behind lie parched deserts desolated by drought, while before are green lands;—so nineteenth-century women are urged on by the pressure of a condition which they have not created, and of whose nature they have not even in many cases a clear intellectual perception, yet which acts upon the whole mass, causing irresistible social movement through its pressure on each isolated unit.

Looking at the modern Woman's Movement from the widest standpoint, and analysing, not isolated phenomena connected with it here and there, but its manifestation as a whole, the conviction is forced upon us that the Woman's Movement of the nineteenth century in its ultimate essence is *The Movement of a Vast Unemployed.*   208–209

Undoubtedly woman suffered, and often suffered heavily, in those primitive societies, but she must always have been clearly conscious, as was the Bantu woman quoted, of the inevitableness of her position. She may have cried out against fate in moments of bitterness, but she must always have recognized her own social importance, and even the anti-sociality of attempting to shirk her obligations, upon the fulfilment of which depended the very life of the society.

Had there arisen a Woman's Movement in any tribe, and had

it been successful, that tribe would have become instantly extinct. The labours of war and the chase were inconsistent with the incessant child-bearing and rearing essential where life is precarious; she could not generally have competed on equal terms with men in war and the chase, when these depended on strength of arm and muscle in wielding spear and axe; she would have forsaken the higher and equally essential labours of society for those for which she was less fitted, and the result must have been the destruction of her society. Not only was a Woman's Movement impossible, but had it been possible it would have been antisocial. Her labour formed the solid superstructure on which her society rested; her submission to her condition was the condition of social health and even national and tribal survival. She suffered and knew she suffered, but she knew also that her condition was inevitable and her society was upheld by her toil.   210

The growing substitution of machinery for human labour in almost all forms of handicraft has diminished the demand for untrained labour; both the family and the State have reached a point where they recognize that the mere production of a human creature, unless there be also the means of fitting it for the complex conditions and duties of modern life, does not increase the wealth or strengh of either state or family, but is a source of weakness and suffering, and there is a steady tendency for persons to marry later and produce fewer offspring as civilization advances in a class or race. So radically has woman's condition changed with regard to this form of labour, that while, in most societies of the past, every woman not physically incapable was a child-bearer, and bore more or less persistently from youth to age, in our own societies at the present day there has arisen a vast body of women compelled, not by any religious enthusiasm, but by the exigencies of modern civilized life, to remain throughout life absolutely celibate and childless, performing no sex function whatever. This phenomenon is accompanied by another equally important, the increase as civilization advances, and especially in our vast cities where it is found in its complete form, of that body of women, who, while not celibate, are also not as a rule child-bearers and mothers, but leading a purely parasitic and non-productive life, drawing their aliment from a society to which they contribute nothing in return.   214

On the other hand, woman may determine not to remain quiescent. As her old fields of labour slip from her under the inevitable changes of modern life, she may determine to find labour in the new and to obtain that training which, whether in the world of handicraft or the mental field of toil, increasingly all-important in our modern world, shall fit her to take as large a share in the labours of her race in the future as in the past. She may determine not to sink into a state of parasitism dependent on her sex functions for support, but to become what she has been through all the ages of the past, the co-worker with man and the sustainer of her society. It is this determination which finds its outcome in the Woman's Movement of our age, a movement entirely new and revolutionary when regarded from one aspect, yet profoundly conservative when regarded from another. New, in that it is an attempt on the part of woman to adapt herself to conditions which have never existed before on the globe; conservative, in that it is an attempt to regain what she has lost. For the hand of the woman who knocks so persistently at the door of the factory for admission to its labour in all its branches is but the hand of the old spinning woman following her loom in its transformation and determined to keep her hold on it; the women who have fought persistently and have at last in a measure won their right to the training that shall fit them to be the physicians of their race are but the "wise woman," "skilled in herbs and all simples," of the past seeking to adapt herself to new conditions. The Woman's

Movement is essentially a movement based on woman's determination to stand where she has always stood beside man as his co-labourer. And the moral fervour which is the general accompaniment of this movement rises from woman's conviction that in attempting to readjust herself to the new conditions of life and retain her hold on the social labours of her race, she is benefiting not herself only, but humanity. 216–217

We are not easily influenced for evil or for good; if we do not learn readily, we do not soon give up that which we have learned; it yields to us a great stability; and as long as, whether as individuals or as a race, we remain on our own soil and among our own native surroundings, though it may make life a little narrow, and somewhat hard, its disadvantages are not serious or vital. But the moment we are placed in close juxtaposition with other races, or enter foreign lands, more especially as rulers or controllers, then that which was an innoxious venial defect becomes a serious, it may be even a deadly, deficiency. 226

The old-fashioned Boer never speaks of war without becoming solemn and reverential, and, metaphorically speaking, taking off his hat. "Man fights; but victory is of God." 255

There are times, when, looking carefully at this nineteenth-century civilization of ours, it appears to us much like that concretion which certain deep-sea creatures build up about themselves out of the sand and rubbish on the deep-sea floor, which after a time becomes hard and solid, and forms their grave. It appears to us that under this vast accumulation of material things, this ceaseless thirst for more and more complex material conditions of life, the human spirit and even the human body are being crushed; that the living creature is building up about itself a tomb, in which it will finally dwindle and die.

We vary endlessly the nature and shape of the garments we wear; but the bodies for which they exist do not grow more powerful or agile; we multiply endlessly the complexity of our foods; but our digestions grow no stronger to deal with them; we build our houses larger and larger, but the span of life for inhabiting them grows no longer: the Bedouin of the Desert inhabits his tent as long: our cities grow vaster and vaster, but our enjoyment of life in them becomes no more intense: our states expand, but the vitality of their component parts rises no higher: we rush from end to end of the earth with the speed of lightning, but we love it no better than men who lived in their valley and went no further than their feet would carry them: we put the whole world under contribution to supply our physical needs, but the breath of life is no sweeter to us than to our forefathers whom the products of one land could satisfy.

For the life of the human creature is but a very little cup in relation to the material goods of life; like the bell of a flower which can hold only one drop of dew, all which you pour in after that can only crush and drown it; it cannot contain it.   260–261

There is music which you have not yet heard—Beethoven's; and there is Mozart's, as sweet as the twitter of the birds when you wake up in your wagon in the early dawn and hear them in the bushes round you in the veld, and as gracious as the sound of the raindrops falling on your roof after a long drought; but do not dream that the man who made it had any relation with the speculators whose loud talk overpowers you with its smartness, or the gorgeously dressed women who make you ashamed of your old black skirt. Believe me, it was made by a man leading a life poor and simple as yours, and who lies in a nameless grave; in poverty and loneliness the music came to him, and he made mankind for ever richer by it; and you can hear it as well in fustian and serge, on a wooden seat as from the king's box, with a band of diamonds above your forehead.

We have also what you have not yet seen, a Moses, cut in stone. When you look at it you are conscious of strength and joy such as you have when you look up at one of our flat-topped African mountains, with the krantzes on its head, casting a deep blue shadow in the early morning;—it is well to look at it; but do not believe that all the millionaires of all the states on earth if they pooled their wealth could ordain that one line of that great figure should have been created: it was shaped by a man who, seeking after beauty and truth, found his God: a man who so lived with his creation that for weeks together he forgot to remove his boots, so that when he did so the skin came off with them: the fine gentlemen of the boulevards and the parks who talk of their superiority to you because they "possess art" (meaning that they have made money enough out of other men's labour to buy the works of dead great men) would hardly have cared to walk down the street with him; his rough, strong face would have befitted better a Boer laager than a circle of modern fashion.   263

Even that knowledge of the conditions of existence which governs the relation of matter with matter, and which yields what is called scientific knowledge, and in a manner seems to mark what is called modern civilization, has yet no causative relation with the greater part of its material phenomena. It does not depend in any way upon the enormous amount of material luxury and wealth concentrated in a few hands which marks our material civilization. It was the Chaldean shepherd watching his flocks at night under a sky as clear and white-studded with stars as that which bends over the Karroo, who first noted the times and seasons of the heavenly bodies. It was the chemist labouring amid the painful fumes of his laboratory with hands as stained by contact with matter as are your sons' to-day when they come in from shearing who first discovered those combinations of atom with the atom, and the reactions of substance on substance, which are letting us slowly a little way into the secret of nature's workshop. It is the mathematician, oblivious of all externals, pondering year after year in his dingy study, with his outlandish garb, who masters at last those laws of relation, the knowledge of which gives to man half his mastery over matter. It is not even the man with the padded shoulders and gilt ornaments upon his dress, who boasts so loudly to you of the superiority of his nineteenth-century weapons of death, who ever made one of them, or even understands how they were made: nor does he always know how to use them! It is not the gaudily dressed man or woman who travels in the first-class compartment of an express train, and looks with wondering contempt at the slow-rolling old ox-wagon which your grandfathers made, who ever made or comprehends one crank or one piston in all that wonderful creation of human labour and thought in which they are luxuriously borne along; or who could invent or shape even the round solid wheel of a primitive donkey-cart.   265–266

The time is very rapidly approaching when the unique relation between the Dutch pastor and his flock will finally have ceased. For the last twenty years the intellect of the Boer race has rapidly been finding openings for itself; the bar, the side-bar, the medical profession, the professor's chair, administrative and political life are absorbing the brilliant youths. The time is very rapidly approaching when the minister will differ from his flocks only in the fact that he has gone through a course of dogmatic theology, and when he will be equalled or excelled in general culture and knowledge of life by the large mass of his congregation; and, with this change, he will take his place side by side with other clergy, whose usefulness is confined to the performance of their ghostly functions; and, with this change also, the Church will cease, save in exceptional cases, to draw the best intellects of the people, as it has done in the past. But we believe that in the future no impartial survey will be possible of the history of South Africa during the last two hundred years without it being perceived how large is the debt which, not the Boer alone, but South Africa generally, owes to the clergy of the Dutch Reformed Churches.   279

Many years ago a Boer woman once inquired of us how it was we never went to any church. We replied that our religion was not at all the same as hers, and that according to our view it was not necessary to go to church. She asked us whether we could explain to her what our religion was like. We replied that we could not, each man's religion was his own concern: and she dropped the matter, nor referred to it again till nearly two years later, when she said: "You told me once that your religion differed from mine; but the more I know you the more I begin to think we must have the same religion. When I sit alone with my sewing I think very far away sometimes; and sometimes it occurs to me like this: If I had many children, and each one spoke a different language, I would try to talk to each child in the language it understood; it would be always me speaking, but in a different language to each child. So, sometimes I think, it is the same God speaking, only He speaks to you and to me in different languages."   283–284

But the difference between a dead and a living religion is vital; the first weighs down the man who carries it; the living religion up-bears him. There is perhaps no life quite worth living without a living religion, under whatever name or form it may be concealed, vivifying and strengthening it.   285

The African woman on her solitary farm may have no inherent power for grasping large wholes, or seeing behind small externals to the moving cause beyond; yet when she sits all the morning sewing in her still front-room, while the children play out in the sunshine by the kraal wall and the flies buzz round, and she sees wherever she raises her head, through the open door, twenty miles of unbroken silent veld with the line of the blue mountains meeting the sky, she is exposed to eight hours of an educative influence entirely distinct from that she would have undergone had she sat in a tenement-room in a city court, and heard her neighbours tramp to and fro on the stairs, and the omnibuses crash in the street, and seen only from her window, when she looked out, the red-brick wall opposite. No man, be he hunter, traveller, or trader, or who or what he may, who has ever been exposed to both orders of influences, will say that their educative effect is the same, or that a man can remain long exposed to either set of influences, the artificial life of cities or the solitude of the desert, without being profoundly modified by it, above all, as to his view of existence as a whole, which is religion.   289

That which the Essenes sought in their rocky caves, which the Buddhist thinker to-day immures himself on his solitary mountain peak to find, which the Christian monks built their monasteries and cloisters to acquire; to supply men artificially with the means of partially attaining to which dim-aisled churches and pillared temples have been reared in the midst of dense populations; which the old Dissenting divine was feeling after when he said: "Spend two hours a day alone in your room with the window open if possible, in quiet and thought; your day will be the stronger and the fuller for it"; and which the Protestant hymn aims at when in its quaint doggerel it says—

> Night is the time pray;
>   The Saviour oft withdrew
> To desert mountains far away;
>   So will his followers do.
> Steal from the world to haunts untrod,
> To hold communion there with God.

—that which religious minds in all centuries and of all races have sought after, has been strangely forced on the African Boer by his silent solitary life amid vast man-unmodified aspects of nature. And with all that he may lack in other directions of knowledge and wisdom, of keenness and versatility, that which the conditions of his life had to teach him, he has learnt. Therefore, though his dogmatic theology is in no sense higher or different from that of others, his religion oftentimes lives when theirs is dead. 290

The consciousness of human solidarity, with its resulting sense of social obligation, has in all ages developed itself in proportion to the nearness of man to man. Initiated in the relation of mother to child, where the union is visible, physical and as complete as is compatible with distinct existence, it has spread itself out successively, as the sentient creature developed, through the relations of family and the tribe to that of nation, and has extended, even though in a partial and undeveloped condition, to the limits of race; but here, almost always, in the average human creature as up to the present time evolved, the growth has stopped. Even the most ordinary man or woman, in the bulk of the societies existing on the earth to-day, is conscious of a certain union with, and more or less strong social obligation towards, the members of his own family; most men are conscious of some sense of solidarity with, and of some social obligation towards, the members of their own national organization; and probably few are wholly unconscious of a certain dim sense of identity with, and a vague (though it may be very vague) sense of obligation towards, men of their own colour and racial development. 293–294

The sooner it is recognized as axiomatic that the distinctions of race are not imaginary and artificial, but real and operative; that they form a barrier so potent that the social instincts and the consciousness of moral obligation continually fail to surmount them; that the men or the nations which may safely be trusted to act with justice and humanity within the limits of their own race are yet, in the majority of cases, wholly incapable of so acting beyond those limits; that only in the case of exceptional individuals gifted with those rare powers of sympathetic insight which enable them, beneath the multitudinous and real differences, mental and physical, which divide wholly distinct races, to see clearly those far more important elements of a common humanity which underlie and unite them, is the instinctive and unconscious extension of social feeling beyond the limits of race possible; that, for all others, wholly just and humane action beyond the limits of their own race, can be only attained as the result of a stern, conscious, unending, mental discipline; and that perhaps no individual man or woman is at the present day so highly developed as regards social instinct as to be certain that they can at all times depend on themselves to act with perfect equity where inter-racial relations are concerned; that no individual is so highly developed morally as to be able wholly to dispense with a most careful intellectual self-examination when dealings with persons of alien race and colour are entered on; and, finally, that the great moral and intellectual expansion which humanity has during the ensuing centuries to undergo, if harmonized human life on the globe is ever to be, is in the direction of extending the social instincts beyond those limits of the family, the nation, and the race, to the humanity beyond those limits:—the sooner we recognize as axiomatic these truths, the quicker will be our progress towards the comprehension and satisfactory solution of racial problems; and, failing to recognize these truths, it is perhaps wholly useless for anyone to attempt to deal with the moral and social aspects of inter-racial questions.   296–297

The African-born farmer, Dutch or English, who has grown up among the natives, has been nursed by them in childhood, often speaks their language, and knows something of their manners and ideas, may hate them; but always, in his heart of hearts, he recognizes them as men; and his very hatred and bitterness is a kind of tribute to the common humanity that he feels binds them. Man only hates man. 308

There is what, for want of a better name, we may define as the financial and speculative attitude towards the native. This is the attitude of the great labour employers. These in South Africa are practically never individuals but great syndicates, companies, and chartered bodies, the individual members of which are seldom or never brought into any personal contact with the natives whose lives they control. In the majority of cases they are non-resident in South Africa, wholly or for the larger part of their lives. For them the native is not a person hated or beloved, but a commercial asset. To these persons the native question sums itself in two words "cheap labour." Their view of the native question is as clear-cut and simple as the outline of a gallows. There is no intricacy or sentiment about it. The native is the machine through the action of which companies and speculators have to extract the wealth of the South African continent; and the more the machinery costs to keep at work, the smaller the percentage of South African wealth which reaches the hands of the speculator.

For them the native problem is in a nutshell: "In how far, and by what means, can the rate of native wages be diminished, so raising profits?" 310

Any attempt on the part of our labouring class to better its position or resist oppressive exactions, being undertaken mainly by men of one colour against men of another, will always immediately awaken, over and above financial opposition, racial prejudice; so that even those white men, whose economic interests are identical with those of the black labourer, may be driven by race antagonism to act with the exactors.   313

The limits are very sharply set, beyond which the greatest Jew or Christian speculators backed by the most powerful princes or plutocracy cannot go. We have no such counterpoise in South Africa. Owing to the difference of colour and race, our great labouring class dare not organize itself and use its strength; and we dare not organize and use it, for fear of awakening the baneful flames of racial antagonism. South Africa is the heaven of the Speculator, the Capitalist and Monopolist. Here, alone, the opposing forces which meet him in every European and civilized country do not exist.   314

The Boer, if he wished to annex a Native territory, says: "The damned Kaffir; I'll take his land from him and divide it among my children." The Frenchman says, if he wishes to possess a territory: "I shall take it for the glory of France and keep it for her honour." And this is noble, direct and manly, if perhaps cruel and unjust.

But the Englishman speaks not so. When he desires an adjoining Native territory, he sighs, and folds his hands; he says: "It's a very sad thing the way these Natives go on! They believe in witches and kill them. I really can't let this go on! It's my duty to interfere. I can't let these poor benighted people go on so!" He says nothing about the coal mines he wants to work in their country or the rich nature of their lands of which he has already got vast grants; so he turns on the Maxim guns, and he kills a few thousands to save the ten witches; and witchcraft is put an end to—but he has the lands and mines, and dishomed and beaten Natives work them for him. How much nobler is the Boer's attitude is obvious. When we want a territory on a larger scale we do not say we are stronger than those people, let us go and kill

them and take command of the land for the glory of the Englishman and the benefit of his trade. We first send some Englishmen
there till the people, knowing our character and that where one
locust comes there come others, grow a little restive and show
some displeasure at our fore-runners; then we draw ourselves
together and say: "It is our duty to defend innocent men and
women trusting to us who have ventured into a strange land"
(how and why they came there we don't inquire), and so we draw
out our guns in the name of a wronged humanity—and so conquer a new land; or we encourage our citizens to buy shares in
a commercial enterprise, lend money may be, and then say: "It
is our duty to take the management of its finance, and eventually
of its government, because it is our duty not to allow innocent
speculators to suffer." Whether the folk in the land will suffer we
leave out of view for the moment, but we dwell on that great duty
—till the land is ours. In the history of the world there was never
a people whose record of relations with other peoples showed so
hideous a record of falsehood and self-deception; other peoples
have lied to each other; but that immeasurably more hideous lie,
the lie told to oneself, has not been common.   347–348

We are asked sometimes: "Well, but what do you intend this
country to be, a black man's country or a white?" We reply we
intend nothing. If the black man cannot labour or bear the strain
and stress of complex civilized life, he will pass away. We need
not degrade and injure ourself by killing him; if *we* cannot work
here, then in time, wholly or in part, the white man will pass away;
and the one best fitted to the land will likely survive—but this we
are determined to do: we will make it a free man's country.
Whether the ultimate race of this country be black, white or
brown, we intend it to be a race permeated with the English
doctrine of the equal right of each human to himself, and the duty
of all to defend the freedom of it.

If it be suggested to us that the Natives of the land are ignorant, we have the reply to make that we are here to teach them all we know if they will learn—if they will not, they must fall.   360–361

We are not blind to the self-seeking and injustice which surround us on every hand. We are not for a moment blind to the fact that sometimes, where we seem to be defending the Native, we are merely using him as a rod with which to strike our white brothers of another speech; we do not forget that English hands have in this country flogged men to death and that, because the man killed was of a dark race, we as an English community have not dared to do more than inflict a fine. We are aware how devoid of any consciousness of large racial function are a mass of our English-speaking folk and how completely devoid of any aim but that of self-betterment are numbers of our units; but, looking these facts directly in the face and allowing all they mean, we yet do not give up hope.

Is it absolutely nothing that in this country there are to be found men who, whether as judges or when serving on juries, are not only incorruptible before the forces of gold or personal interest but before the much more terrible corruption of racial prejudice and passion?   363

A man far out at sea on a dark night, struggling with the waves in his small boat, sees far away a light he thinks to be the harbour light and strikes towards it; knowing he may be mistaken, and that long before daybreak man and boat may be engulfed, he still strikes towards it, labouring without certainty of ever reaching it but with unalterable will and determination, because it is the only light he sees.   366

Dreams

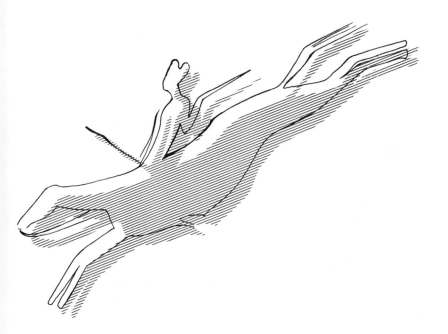

From Three Dreams in a Desert

I saw a desert and I saw a woman coming out of it. And she came to the bank of a dark river; and the bank was steep and high. And on it an old man met her, who had a long white beard; and a stick that curled was in his hand, and on it was written Reason. And he asked her what she wanted; and she said, "I am woman; and I am seeking for the land of Freedom."

And he said, "It is before you."

And she said, "I see nothing before me but a dark flowing river, and a bank steep and high, and cuttings here and there with heavy sand in them."

And he said, "And beyond that?"

She said, "I see nothing, but sometimes, when I shade my eyes with my hand, I think I see on the further bank trees and hills, and the sun shining on them!"

He said, "That is the Land of Freedom."

She said, "How am I to get there?"

He said, "There is one way, and one only. Down the banks of Labour, through the water of Suffering. There is no other."

She said, "Is there no bridge?"

He answered, "None."

She said, "Is the water deep?"

He said, "Deep."

She said, "Is the floor worn?"

He said, "It is. Your foot may slip at any time, and you may be lost."

She said, "Have any crossed already?"

He said, "Some have *tried!*"

She said, "Is there a track to show where the best fording is?"

He said, "It has to be made."

She shaded her eyes with her hand; and she said, "I will go."

And he said, "You must take off the clothes you wore in the desert: they are dragged down by them who go into the water so clothed."

And she threw from her gladly the mantle of Ancient-received-opinions she wore, for it was worn full of holes. And she took the girdle from her waist that she had treasured so long, and the moths flew out of it in a cloud. And he said, "Take the shoes of dependence off your feet."

And she stood there naked, but for one white garment that clung close to her.

And he said, "That you may keep. So they wear clothes in the Land of Freedom. In the water it buoys; it always swims."

And I saw on its breast was written Truth; and it was white; the sun had not often shone on it; the other clothes had covered it up. And he said, "Take this stick; hold it fast. In that day when it slips from your hand you are lost. Put it down before you; feel your way: where it cannot find a bottom do not set your foot."

And she said, "I am ready; let me go."

And he said, "No—but stay; what is that—in your breast?"

She was silent.

He said, "Open it, and let me see."

And she opened it. And against her breast was a tiny thing, who drank from it, and the yellow curls above his forehead pressed against it; and his knees were drawn up to her, and he held her breast fast with his hands.

And Reason said, "Who is he, and what is he doing here?"

And she said, "See his little wings—"

And Reason said, "Put him down."

And she said, "He is asleep, and he is drinking! I will carry him to the Land of Freedom. He has been a child so long, so long, I have carried him. In the Land of Freedom he will be a man. We will walk together there, and his great white wings will overshadow me. He has lisped one word only to me in the desert—'Passion!' I have dreamed he might learn to say 'Friendship' in that land."

And Reason said, "Put him down!"

And she said, "I will carry him so—with one arm, and with the other I will fight the water."

He said, "Lay him down on the ground. When you are in the water you will forget to fight, you will think only of him. Lay him down." He said, "He will not die. When he finds you have left him alone he will open his wings and fly. He will be in the Land of Freedom before you. Those who reach the Land of Freedom, the first hand they see stretching down the bank to help them shall be Love's. He will be a man then, not a child. In your breast he cannot thrive; put him down that he may grow."

And she took her bosom from his mouth, and he bit her, so that the blood ran down on to the ground. And she laid him down on the earth; and she covered her wound. And she bent and stroked his wings. And I saw the hair on her forehead turned white as snow, and she had changed from youth to age.

And she stood far off on the bank of the river. And she said, "For what do I go to this far land which no one has ever reached? *Oh, I am alone! I am utterly alone!*"

And Reason, that old man, said to her, "Silence! what do you hear?"

And she listened intently, and she said, "I hear a sound of feet, a thousand times ten thousand and thousands of thousands, and they beat this way!"

He said, "They are the feet of those that shall follow you. Lead on! make a track to the water's edge! Where you stand now, the ground will be beaten flat by ten thousand times ten thousand feet." And he said, "Have you seen the locusts how they cross a stream? First one comes down to the water-edge, and it is swept away, and then another comes and then another, and then another, and at last with their bodies piled up a bridge is built and the rest pass over."

She said, "And, of those that come first, some are swept away, and are heard of no more; their bodies do not even build the bridge?"

"And are swept away, and are heard of no more—and what of that?" he said.

"And what of that—" she said.'

"They make a track to the water's edge."

"They make a track to the water's edge—." And she said, "Over that bridge which shall be built with our bodies, who will pass?"

He said, *"The entire human race."*

And the woman grasped her staff.

And I saw her turn down that dark path to the river.   75–83

And I dreamed a dream.

I dreamed I saw a land. And on the hills walked brave women and brave men, hand in hand. And they looked into each other's eyes, and they were not afraid.

And I saw the women also hold each other's hands.

And I said to him beside me, "What place is this?"

And he said, "This is heaven."

And I said, "Where is it?"

And he answered, "On earth."

And I said, "When shall these things be?"

And he answered, "In the Future."   84

From *In a Ruined Chapel*

A man cried up to God, and God sent down an angel to help him; and the angel came back and said, "I cannot help that man."

God said, "How is it with him?"

And the angel said, "He cries out continually that one has injured him; and he would forgive him and he cannot."

God said, "What have you done for him?"

The angel said, "All—. I took him by the hand, and I said, 'See, when other men speak ill of that man do you speak well of him; secretly, in ways he shall not know, serve him; if you have anything you value share it with him, so, serving him, you will at last come to feel possession in him, and you will forgive.' And he said, 'I will do it.' Afterwards, as I passed by in the dark of night, I heard one crying out, 'I have done all. It helps nothing! My speaking well of him helps me nothing! If I share my heart's blood with him, is the burning within me less? I cannot forgive; I cannot forgive! Oh, God, I cannot forgive!'

"I said to him, 'See here, look back on all your past. See from your childhood all smallness, all indirectness that has been yours; look well at it, and in its light do you not see every man your brother? Are you so sinless you have right to hate?'

"He looked, and said, 'Yes, you are right; I too have failed, and I forgive my fellow. Go, I am satisfied; I have forgiven'; and he laid him down peacefully and folded his hands on his breast, and I thought it was well with him. But scarcely had my wings rustled and I turned to come up here, when I heard one crying out on earth again, 'I cannot forgive! I cannot forgive! Oh, God, God, I cannot forgive! It is better to die than to hate! I cannot forgive! I cannot forgive!' And I went and stood outside his door in the dark, and I heard him cry, 'I have not sinned so, not so! If I have torn my fellows' flesh ever so little, I have kneeled down and kissed the wound with my mouth till it was healed. I have not willed that any soul should be lost through hate of me. If they have but fancied that I wronged them I have lain down on the ground before them that they might tread on me, and so, seeing my humiliation, forgive and not be lost through hating me; they have not cared that my soul should be lost; they have not willed to save me; they have not tried that I should forgive them!'

"I said to him, 'See here, be thou content; do *not* forgive: forget this soul and its injury; go on your way. In the next world perhaps—'

"He cried, 'Go from me, you understand nothing! What is the next world to me! I am lost now, to-day. I cannot see the sunlight shine, the dust is in my throat, the sand is in my eyes! Go from me, you know nothing! Oh, once again before I die to see that the world is beautiful! Oh, God, God, I cannot live and not love. I cannot live and hate. Oh, God, God, God!' So I left him crying out and came back here."

God said, "This man's soul must be saved."

And the angel said, "How?"

God said, "Go down you, and save it."

The angel said, "What more shall I do?"

Then God bent down and whispered in the angel's ear, and the angel spread out its wings and went down to earth. . . .

The angel went down and found the man with the bitter heart and took him by the hand, and led him to a certain spot.

Now the man wist not where it was the angel would take him nor what he would show him there. And when they came the angel shaded the man's eyes with his wing, and when he moved it the man saw somewhat on the earth before them. For God had given it to that angel to unclothe a human soul; to take from it all those outward attributes of form, and colour, and age, and sex, whereby one man is known from among his fellows and is marked off from the rest, and the soul lay before them, bare, as a man turning his eye inwards beholds himself.

They saw its past, its childhood, the tiny life with the dew upon it; they saw its youth when the dew was melting, and the creature raised its Liliputian mouth to drink from a cup too large for it, and they saw how the water spilt; they saw its hopes that were never realized; they saw its hours of intellectual blindness, men call sin; they saw its hours of all-radiating insight, which men call righteousness; they saw its hour of strength, when it leaped to its feet crying, "I am omnipotent"; its hour of weakness, when it fell to the earth and grasped dust only; they saw what it might have been, but never would be.

The man bent forward.

And the angel said, "What is it?"

He answered, "It is *I!* it is myself!"

And he went forward as if he would have lain his heart against it; but the angel held him back and covered his eyes.

Now God had given power to the angel further to unclothe that soul, to take from it all those outward attributes of time and place and circumstance whereby the individual life is marked off from the life of the whole.

Again the angel uncovered the man's eyes, and he looked. He saw before him that which in its tiny drop reflects the whole universe; he saw that which marks within itself the step of the furthest star, and tells how the crystal grows under the ground where no eye has seen it; that which is where the germ in the egg stirs; which moves the outstretched fingers of the little newborn babe, and keeps the leaves of the trees pointing upward; which moves where the jelly-fish sail alone on the sunny seas, and is where the lichens form on the mountains' rocks.

And the man looked.

And the angel touched him.

But the man bowed his head and shuddered. He whispered—
"*It is God!*"

And the angel re-covered the man's eyes. And when he uncovered them there was one walking from them a little way off;—for the angel had re-clothed the soul in its outward form and vesture —and the man knew who it was.

And the angel said, "Do you know him?"

And the man said, "I know him," and he looked after the figure.

And the angel said, "Have you forgiven him?"

But the man said, *"How beautiful my brother is!"*

And the angel looked into the man's eyes, and he shaded his own face with his wing from the light. He laughed softly and went up to God.

But the men were together on earth.   103–111

Life's Gifts

I saw a woman sleeping. In her sleep she dreamt Life stood before her, and held in each hand a gift—in the one Love, in the other Freedom. And she said to the woman, "Choose!"

And the woman waited long: and she said, "Freedom!"

And Life said, "Thou hast well chosen. If thou hadst said, 'Love,' I would have given thee that thou didst ask for; and I would have gone from thee, and returned to thee no more. Now, the day will come when I shall return. In that day I shall bear both gifts in one hand."

I heard the woman laugh in her sleep.   115–116

A Dream of Wild Bees

A mother sat alone at an open window. Through it came the voices of the children as they played under the acacia-trees, and the breath of the hot afternoon air. In and out of the room flew the bees, the wild bees, with their legs yellow with pollen, going to and from the acacia-trees, droning all the while. She sat on a low chair before the table and darned. She took her work from the great basket that stood before her on the table: some lay on her knee and half covered the book that rested there. She watched the needle go in and out; and the dreary hum of the bees and the noise of the children's voices became a confused murmur in her ears, as she worked slowly and more slowly. Then the bees, the long-legged wasp-like fellows who make no honey, flew closer and closer to her head, droning. Then she grew more and more drowsy, and she laid her hand, with the stocking over it, on the edge of the table, and leaned her head upon it. And the voices of the children outside grew more and more dreamy, came now far, now near; then she did not hear them, but she felt under her heart where the ninth child lay. Bent forward and sleeping there, with the bees flying about her head, she had a weird brain-picture; she thought the bees lengthened and lengthened themselves out and became human creatures and moved round and round her. Then one came to her softly, saying, "Let me lay my hand upon thy side where the child sleeps. If I shall touch him he shall be as I."

She asked, "Who are you?"

And he said, "I am Health. Whom I touch will have always the red blood dancing in his veins; he will not know weariness nor pain; life will be a long laugh to him."

"No," said another, "let me touch; for I am Wealth. If I touch him material care shall not feed on him. He shall live on the blood and sinews of his fellow-men, if he will; and what his eye lusts for, his hand will have. He shall not know 'I want.' " And the child lay still like lead.

And another said, "Let me touch him: I am Fame. The man I touch, I lead to a high hill where all men may see him. When he dies he is not forgotten, his name rings down the centuries, each echoes it on to his fellows. Think—not to be forgotten through the ages!"

And the mother lay breathing steadily, but in the brain-picture they pressed closer to her.

"Let me touch the child," said one, "for I am Love. If I touch him he shall not walk through life alone. In the greatest dark, when he puts out his hand he shall find another hand by it. When the world is against him, another shall say, 'You and I!'" And the child trembled.

But another pressed close and said, "Let me touch; for I am Talent. I can do all things—that have been done before. I touch the soldier, the statesman, the thinker, and the politician who succeed; and the writer who is never before his time, and never behind it. If I touch the child he shall not weep for failure."

About the mother's head the bees were flying, touching her with their long tapering limbs; and, in her brain-picture, out of the shadow of the room came one with sallow face, deep-lined, the cheeks drawn into hollows, and a mouth smiling quiveringly. He stretched out his hand. And the mother drew back, and cried, "Who are you?" He answered nothing; and she looked up between his eyelids. And she said, "What can you give the child— health?" And he said, "The man I touch, there wakes up in his blood a burning fever, that shall lick his blood as fire. The fever that I will give him shall be cured when his life is cured."

"You give wealth?"

He shook his head. "The man whom I touch, when he bends

to pick up gold, he sees suddenly a light over his head in the sky; while he looks up to see it, the gold slips from between his fingers, or sometimes another passing takes it from them."

"Fame?"

He answered, "Likely not. For the man I touch there is a path traced out in the sand by a finger which no man sees. That he must follow. Sometimes it leads almost to the top, and then turns down suddenly into the valley. He must follow it, though none else sees the tracing."

"Love?"

He said, "He shall hunger for it—but he shall not find it. When he stretches out his arms to it, and would lay his heart against a thing he loves, then, far off along the horizon he shall see a light play. He must go towards it. The thing he loves will not journey with him; he must travel alone. When he presses somewhat to his burning heart, crying, 'Mine, mine, my own!' he shall hear a voice —'Renounce! renounce! this is not thine!' "

"He shall succeed?"

He said, "He shall fail. When he runs with others they shall reach the goal before him. For strange voices shall call to him and strange lights shall beckon him, and he must wait and listen. And this shall be the strangest: far off across the burning sands where, to other men, there is only the desert's waste, he shall see a blue sea! On that sea the sun shines always, and the water is blue as burning amethyst, and the foam is white on the shore. A great land rises from it, and he shall see upon the mountain-tops burning gold."

The mother said, "He shall reach it?"

And he smiled curiously.

She said, "It is real?"

And he said, "What *is* real?"

And she looked up between his half-closed eyelids, and said, "Touch."

And he leaned forward and laid his hand upon the sleeper, and whispered to it, smiling; and this only she heard—*"This shall be thy reward—that the ideal shall be real to thee."*

And the child trembled; but the mother slept on heavily and her brain-picture vanished. But deep within her the antenatal thing that lay here had a dream. In those eyes that had never seen the day, in that half-shaped brain was a sensation of light! Light —that it never had seen. Light—that perhaps it never should see. Light—that existed somewhere!

And already it had its reward: the Ideal was real to it.   89–96

The Sunlight Lay Across My Bed—

In the dark one night I lay upon my bed. I heard the policeman's feet beat on the pavement; I heard the wheels of carriages roll home from houses of entertainment; I heard a woman's laugh below my window—and then I fell asleep. And in the dark I dreamt a dream. I dreamt God took my soul to Hell.

Hell was a fair place; the water of the lake was blue.
I said to God, "I like this place."
God said, "Ay, dost thou!"
Birds sang, turf came to the water-edge, and trees grew from it. Away off among the trees I saw beautiful women walking. Their clothes were of many delicate colours and clung to them, and they were tall and graceful and had yellow hair. Their robes trailed over the grass. They glided in and out among the trees, and over their heads hung yellow fruit like large pears of melted gold.
I said, "It is very fair; I would go up and taste the—"
God said, "Wait."
And after a while I noticed a very fair woman pass: she looked

this way and that, and drew down a branch, and it seemed she kissed the fruit upon it softly, and went on her way, and her dress made no rustle as she passed over the grass. And when I saw her no more, from among the stems came another woman fair as she had been, in a delicate tinted robe; she looked this way and that. When she saw no one there she drew down the fruit, and when she had looked over it to find a place, she put her mouth to it softly, and went away. And I saw other and other women come, making no noise, and they glided away also over the grass.

And I said to God, "What are they doing?"

God said, "They are poisoning."

And I said, "How?"

God said, "They touch it with their lips, when they have made a tiny wound in it with their fore-teeth they set in it that which is under their tongues: they close it with their lip—that no man may see the place, and pass on."

I said to God, "Why do they do it?"

God said, "That another may not eat."

I said to God, "But if they poison all then none dare eat; what do they gain?"

God said, "Nothing."

I said, "Are they not afraid they themselves may bite where another has bitten?"

God said, "They are afraid. In Hell all men fear."

He called me further. And the water of the lake seemed less blue.

Then, to the right among the trees were men working. And I said to God, "I should like to go and work with them. Hell must be a very fruitful place, the grass is so green."

God said, "Nothing grows in the garden they are making."

We stood looking; and I saw them working among the bushes, digging holes, but in them they set nothing; and when they had covered them with sticks and earth each went a way off and sat behind the bushes watching; and I noticed that as each walked he set his foot down carefully looking where he trod. I said to God, "What are they doing?"

God said, "Making pitfalls into which their fellows may sink."

I said to God, "Why do they do it?"

God said, "Because each thinks that when his brother falls he will rise."

I said to God, "How will he rise?"

God said, "He will not rise."

And I saw their eyes gleam from behind the bushes.

I said to God, "Are these men sane?"

God said, "They are not sane; there is no sane man in Hell."

And he told me to come further.

And I looked where I trod.

And we came where Hell opened into a plain, and a great house stood there. Marble pillars upheld the roof, and white marble steps led up to it. The wind of heaven blew through it. Only at the back hung a thick curtain. Fair men and women there feasted at long tables. They danced, and I saw the robes of women flutter in the air and heard the laugh of strong men. What they feasted with was wine; they drew it from large jars which stood somewhat in the background, and I saw the wine sparkle as they drew it.

And I said to God, "I should like to go up and drink." And God said, "Wait." And I saw men coming in to the Banquet House; they came in from the back and lifted the corner of the curtain at the sides and crept in quickly; and they let the curtain fall behind them; they bore great jars they could hardly carry. And the men and women crowded round them, and the newcomers opened their jars and gave them of the wine to drink; and I saw that the women drank even more greedily than the men. And when others had well drunken they set the jars among the old ones beside the wall, and took their places at the table. And I saw that some of the jars were very old and mildewed and dusty, but others had still drops of new must on them and shone from the furnace.

And I said to God, "What is that?" For amid the sound of the singing, and over the dancing of feet, and over the laughing across the wine-cups I heard a cry.

And God said, "Stand a way off."

And he took me where I saw both sides of the curtain. Behind the house was the wine-press where the wine was made. I saw the grapes crushed, and I heard them cry. I said, "Do not they on the other side hear it?"

God said, "The curtain is thick; they are feasting."

And I said, "But the men who came in last. They saw?"

God said, "They let the curtain fall behind them—and they forget!"

I said, "How came they by their jars of wine?"

God said, "In the treading of the press these are they who came to the top; they have climbed out over the edge, and filled their jars from below, and have gone into the house."

And I said, "And if they had fallen as they climbed—?"

God said, "They had been wine."

I stood a way off watching in the sunshine, and I shivered.

God lay in the sunshine watching too.

Then there rose one among the feasters, who said, "My brethren, let us pray!"

And all the men and women rose: and strong men bowed their heads, and mothers folded their little children's hands together, and turned their faces upwards, to the roof. And he who first had risen stood at the table head, and stretched out both his hands, and his beard was long and white, and his sleeves and his beard had been dipped in wine; and because the sleeves were wide and full they held much wine, and it dropped down upon the floor.

And he cried, "My brothers and my sisters, let us pray."

And all the men and women answered, "Let us pray."

He cried, "For this fair banquet-house we thank thee, Lord."
And all the men and women said, "We thank thee, Lord."
"Thine is this house, dear Lord."
"Thine is this house."
"For us hast thou made it."
"For us."
"Oh, fill our jars with wine, dear Lord."
"Our jars with wine."
"Give peace and plenty in our time, dear Lord."
"Peace and plenty in our time"—I said to God, "Whom is it they are talking to?" God said, "Do *I* know whom they speak of?" And I saw they were looking up at the roof; but out in the sunshine, God lay.
"—dear Lord!"
"Dear Lord."
"Our children's children, Lord, shall rise and call thee blessed."
"Our children's children, Lord."—I said to God, "The grapes are crying!" God said, "Still! *I* hear them"—"shall call thee blessed."
"Shall call thee blessed."
"Pour forth more wine upon us, Lord."
"More wine."
"More wine."
"More wine."
"More wine!"
"Wine!!"
"Wine!!"
"Wine!!!"
"Dear Lord!"
Then men and women sat down and the feast went on. And mothers poured out wine and fed their little children with it, and men held up the cup to women's lips and cried, "Beloved! drink,"

and women filled their lovers' flagons and held them up; and yet the feast went on.

And after a while I looked, and I saw the curtain that hung behind the house moving.

I said to God, "Is it a wind?"

God said, "A wind."

And it seemed to me, that against the curtain I saw pressed the forms of men and women. And after a while the feasters saw it move, and they whispered, one to another. Then some rose and gathered the most worn-out cups, and in them they put what was left at the bottom of other vessels. Mothers whispered to their children, "Do not drink all, save a little drop when you have drunk." And when they had collected all the dregs they slipped the cups out under the bottom of the curtain without lifting it. After a while the curtain left off moving.

I said to God, "How is it so quiet?"

He said, "They have gone away to drink it."

I said, "*They* drink it—*their own*!"

God said, "It comes from this side of the curtain, and they are very thirsty."

Then the feast went on, and after a while I saw a small, white hand slipped in below the curtain's edge along the floor; and it motioned towards the wine jars.

And I said to God, "Why is that hand so bloodless?"

And God said, "It is a wine-pressed hand."

And men saw it and started to their feet; and women cried, and ran to the great wine jars, and threw their arms around them, and cried, "Ours, our own, our beloved!" and twined their long hair about them.

I said to God, "Why are they frightened of that one small hand?"

God answered, "Because it is so white."

And men ran in a great company towards the curtain, and

struggled there. I heard them strike upon the floor. And when they moved away the curtain hung smooth and still; and there was a small stain upon the floor.

I said to God, "Why do they not wash it out?"

God said, "They cannot."

And they took small stones and put them down along the edge of the curtain to keep it down. Then the men and women sat down again at the tables.

And I said to God, "Will these stones keep it down?"

God said, "What think you?"

I said, "If the wind blew—"

God said, "If the wind blew?"

And the feast went on.

And suddenly I cried to God, "If one should rise among them, even of themselves, and start up from the table and should cast away his cup, and cry, 'My brothers and my sisters, stay! what is it that we drink?—and with his sword should cut in two the curtain, and holding wide the fragments, cry, 'Brothers, sisters, see! it is not wine, not wine! not wine! My brothers, oh, my sisters —!' and he should overturn the—"

God said, "Be still!—see there."

I looked: before the banquet-house, among the grass, I saw a row of mounds, flowers covered them, and gilded marble stood at their heads. I asked God what they were.

He answered, "They are the graves of those who rose up at the feast and cried."

And I asked God how they came there.

He said, "The men of the banquet-house rose and cast them down backwards."

I said, "Who buried them?"

God said, "The men who cast them down."

I said, "How came it that they threw them down, and then set marble over them?"

God said, "Because the bones cried out, they covered them."

And among the grass and weeds I saw an unburied body lying; and I asked God why it was.

God said, "Because it was thrown down only yesterday. In a little while, when the flesh shall have fallen from its bones, they will bury it also, and plant flowers over it."

And still the feast went on.

Men and women sat at the tables quaffing great bowls. Some rose, and threw their arms about each other, and danced and sang. They pledged each other in the wine, and kissed each other's blood-red lips.

Higher and higher grew the revels.

Men, when they had drunk till they could no longer, threw what was left in their glasses up to the roof, and let it fall back in cascades. Women dyed their children's garments in the wine, and fed them on it till their tiny mouths were red. Sometimes, as the dancers whirled, they overturned a vessel, and their garments were bespattered. Children sat upon the floor with great bowls of wine, and swam rose-leaves on it, for boats. They put their hands in the wine and blew large red bubbles.

And higher and higher grew the revels, and wilder the dancing and louder and louder the singing. But here and there among the revellers were those who did not revel. I saw that at the tables here and there were men who sat with their elbows on the board and hands shading their eyes; they looked into the wine-cup beneath them, and did not drink. And when one touched them lightly on the shoulder, bidding them to rise and dance and sing, they started, and then looked down, and sat there watching the wine in the cup, but they did not move.

And here and there I saw a woman sit apart. The others danced and sang and fed their children, but she sat silent with her head aside as though she listened. Her little children plucked her gown; she did not see them; she was listening to some sound, but she did not stir.

The revels grew higher. Men drank till they could drink no longer, and lay their heads upon the table sleeping heavily. Women who could dance no more leaned back on the benches with their heads against their lovers' shoulders. Little children, sick with wine, lay down upon the edges of their mothers' robes. Sometimes, a man rose suddenly, and as he staggered struck the tables and overthrew the benches; some leaned upon the balustrades sick unto death. Here and there one rose who staggered to the wine jars and lay down beside them. He turned the wine tap, but sleep overcame him as he lay there, and the wine ran out.

Slowly the thin, red stream ran across the white marbled floor; it reached the stone steps; slowly, slowly, slowly it trickled down, from step to step, from step to step: then it sank into the earth. A thin white smoke rose up from it.

I was silent; I could not breathe, but God called me to come further.

And after I had travelled for a while I came where on seven hills lay the ruins of a mighty banquet-house larger and stronger than the one which I had seen standing.

I said to God, "What did the men who built it here?"

God said, "They feasted."

I said, "On what?"

God said, "On wine."

And I looked; and it seemed to me that behind the ruins lay still a large circular hollow within the earth where a foot of the wine-press had stood.

I said to God, "How came it that this large house fell?"

God said, "Because the earth was sodden."

He called me to come further.

And at last we came upon a hill where blue waters played, and white marble lay upon the earth. I said to God, "What was here once?"

God said, "A pleasure house."

I looked, and at my feet great pillars lay. I cried aloud for joy to God, "The marble blossoms!"

God said, "Ay, 'twas a fairy house. There has not been one like to it, nor ever shall be. The pillars and the porticoes blossomed; and the wine-cups were as gathered flowers: on this side all the curtain was broidered with fair designs, the stitching was of gold."

I said to God, "How came it that it fell!"

God said, "On the side of the wine-press it was dark."

And as we travelled, we came where lay a mighty ridge of sand, and a dark river ran there; and there rose two vast mounds.

I said to God, "They are very mighty."

God said, "Ay, exceeding great."

And I listened.

God asked me what I was listening to.

And I said, "A sound of weeping, and I hear the sound of strokes, but I cannot tell whence it comes."

God said, "It is the echo of the wine-press lingering still among the coping-stones upon the mounds. A banquet-house stood here."

And he called me to come further.

Upon a barren hill-side, where the soil was arid, God called me to stand still. And I looked around.

God said, "There was a feasting-house here once upon a time."

I said to God, "I see no mark of any!"

God said, "There was not left one stone upon another that has not been thrown down." And I looked round; and on the hill-side was a lonely grave.

I said to God, "What lies there?"

He said, "A vine truss, bruised in the wine-press!"

And at the head of the grave stood a cross, and on its foot lay a crown of thorns.

And as I turned to go, I looked backward. The wine-press and the banquet-house were gone; but the grave yet stood.

And when I came to the edge of a long ridge there opened out before me a wide plain of sand. And when I looked downward I saw great stones lie shattered; and the desert sand had half covered them over.

I said to God, "There is writing on them, but I cannot read it."

And God blew aside the desert sand, and I read the writing: "Weighed in the balance, and found—" but the last word was wanting.

And I said to God, "It was a banquet-house."

God said, "Ay, a banquet-house."

I said, "There was a wine-press here?"

God said, "There was a wine-press."

I asked no further question. I was very weary; I shaded my eyes with my hand, and looked through the pink evening light.

Far off, across the sand, I saw two figures standing. With wings upfolded high above their heads, and stern faces set, neither man nor beast, they looked out across the desert sand, watching, watching, watching! I did not ask God what they were, for I knew what the answer would be.

And, further and yet further, in the evening light, I looked with my shaded eyes.

Far off, where the sands were thick and heavy, I saw a solitary pillar standing: the crown had fallen, and the sand had buried it. On the broken pillar sat a grey owl-of-the-desert, with folded wings; and in the evening light I saw the desert fox creep past it, trailing his brush across the sand.

Further, yet further, as I looked across the desert, I saw the sand gathered into heaps as though it covered something.

I cried to God, "Oh, I am so weary."

God said, "You have seen only one half of Hell."

I said, "I cannot see more, I am afraid of Hell. In my own

narrow little path I dare not walk because I think that one has dug a pitfall for me; and if I put my hand to take a fruit I draw it back again because I think it has been kissed already. If I look out across the plains, the mounds are burial heaps; and when I pass among the stones I hear them crying aloud. When I see men dancing I hear the time beaten in with sobs; and their wine is living! Oh, I cannot bear Hell!"

God said, "Where will you go?"

I said, "To the earth from which I came; it was better there."

And God laughed at me; and I wondered why he laughed.

God said, "Come, and I will show you Heaven."

And partly I awoke. It was still and dark; the sound of the carriages had died in the street; the woman who laughed was gone; and the policeman's tread was heard no more. In the dark it seemed as if a great hand lay upon my heart, and crushed it. I tried to breathe and tossed from side to side; and then again I fell asleep, and dreamed.

God took me to the edge of that world. It ended. I looked down. The gulf, it seemed to me, was fathomless, and then I saw two bridges crossing it that both sloped upwards.

I said to God, "Is there no other way by which men cross it?"

God said, "One; it rises far from here and slopes straight upwards."

I asked God what the bridges' names were.

God said, "What matter for the names? Call them the Good, the True, the Beautiful, if you will—you will yet not understand them."

I asked God how it was I could not see the third.

God said, "It is seen only by those who climb it."

I said, "Do they all lead to one heaven?"

God said, "All Heaven is one: nevertheless some parts are higher than others; those who reach the higher may always go down to rest in the lower; but those in the lower may not have strength to climb to the higher; nevertheless the light is all one."

And I saw over the bridge nearest me, which was wider than the other, countless footmarks go. I asked God why so many went over it.

God said, "It slopes less deeply, and leads to the first heaven."

And I saw that some of the footmarks were of feet returning. I asked God how it was.

He said, "No man who has once entered Heaven ever leaves it; but some, when they have gone half way, turn back, because they are afraid there is no land beyond."

I said, "Has none ever returned?"

God said, "No; once in Heaven always in Heaven."

And God took me over. And when we came to one of the great doors—for Heaven has more doors than one, and they are all open—the posts rose up so high on either side I could not see the top, nor indeed if there were any.

And it seemed to me so wide that all Hell could go in through it.

I said to God, "Which is the larger, Heaven or Hell?"

God said, "Hell is as wide, but Heaven is deeper. All Hell could be engulfed in Heaven, but all Heaven could not be engulfed in Hell."

And we entered. It was a still great land. The mountains rose on every hand, and there was a pale clear light; and I saw it came from the rocks and stones. I asked God how it was.

But God did not answer me.

I looked and wondered, for I had thought Heaven would be otherwise. And after a while it began to grow brighter, as if the day were breaking, and I asked God if the sun were not going to rise.

God said, "No; we are coming to where the people are."

And as we went on it grew brighter and brighter till it was

burning day; and on the rock were flowers blooming, and trees blossomed at the roadside; and streams of water ran everywhere, and I heard the birds singing; I asked God where they were.

God said, "It is the people calling to one another."

And when we came nearer I saw them walking, and they shone as they walked. I asked God how it was they wore no covering.

God said, "Because all their body gives the light; they dare not cover any part."

And I asked God what they were doing.

God said, "Shining on the plants that they may grow."

And I saw that some were working in companies, and some alone, but most were in twos, sometimes two men and sometimes two women; but generally there was one man and one woman; and I asked God how it was.

God said, "When one man and one woman shine together, it makes the most perfect light. Many plants need that for their growing. Nevertheless, there are more kinds of plants in Heaven than one, and they need many kinds of light."

And one from among the people came running towards me; and when he came near it seemed to me that he and I had played together when we were little children, and that we had been born on the same day. And I told God what I felt; God said, "All men feel so in Heaven when another comes towards them."

And he who ran towards me held my hand, and led me through the bright lights. And when we came among the trees he sang aloud, and his companion answered, and it was a woman, and he showed me to her. She said, "He must have water"; and she took some in her hands, and fed me (I had been afraid to drink of the water in Hell), and they gathered fruit for me, and gave it me to eat. They said, "We shone long to make it ripen," and they laughed together as they saw me eat it.

The man said, "He is very weary; he must sleep" (for I had not dared to sleep in Hell), and he laid my head on his companion's knee and spread her hair out over me. I slept, and all the while in my sleep I thought I heard the birds calling across me. And when I woke it was like early morning, with the dew on everything.

And the man took my hand and led me to a hidden spot among the rocks. The ground was very hard, but out of it were sprouting tiny plants, and there was a little stream running. He said, "This is a garden we are making, no one else knows of it. We shine here every day; see, the ground has cracked with our shining, and this little stream is bursting out. See, the flowers are growing."

And he climbed on the rocks and picked from above two little flowers with dew on them, and gave them to me. And I took one in each hand; my hands shone as I held them. He said, "This garden is for all when it is finished." And he went away to his companion, and I went out into the great pathway.

And as I walked in the light I heard a loud sound of much singing. And when I came nearer I saw one with closed eyes, singing, and his fellows were standing round him; and the light on the closed eyes was brighter than anything I had seen in Heaven. I asked one who it was. And he said, "Hush! Our singing bird."

And I asked why the eyes shone so.

And he said, "They cannot see, and we have kissed them till they shone so."

And the people gathered closer round him.

And when I went a little further I saw a crowd crossing among the trees of light with great laughter. When they came close I saw they carried one without hands or feet. And a light came from the maimed limbs so bright that I could not look at them.

And I said to one, "What is it?"

He answered, "This is our brother who once fell and lost his hands and feet, and since then he cannot help himself; but we have touched the maimed stumps so often that now they shine brighter than anything in Heaven. We pass him on that he may shine on things that need much heat. No one is allowed to keep him long, he belongs to all"; and they went on among the trees.

I said to God, "This is a strange land. I had thought blindness and maimedness were great evils. Here men make them to a rejoicing."

God said, "Didst thou then think that love had *need* of eyes and hands!"

And I walked down the shining way with palms on either hand. I said to God, "Ever since I was a little child and sat alone and cried, I have dreamed of this land, and now I will not go away again. I will stay here and shine." And I began to take off my garments, that I might shine as others in that land; but when I looked down I saw my body gave no light. I said to God, "How is it?"

God said, "Is there no dark blood in your heart; is it bitter against none?"

And I said, "Yes—"; and I thought—"Now is the time when I will tell God, that which I have been meaning to tell him all along, how badly my fellow-men have treated me. How they have misunderstood me. How I have intended to be magnanimous and generous to them, and they—." And I began to tell God; but when I looked down all the flowers were withering under my breath, and I was silent.

And God called me to come up higher, and I gathered my mantle about me and followed him.

And the rocks grew higher and steeper on every side; and we came at last to a place where a great mountain rose, whose top was lost in the clouds. And on its side I saw men working; and they picked at the earth with huge picks; and I saw that they laboured mightily. And some laboured in companies, but most laboured singly. And I saw the drops of sweat fall from their foreheads, and the muscles of their arms stand out with labour.

And I said, "I had not thought in heaven to see men labour so!" And I thought of the garden where men sang and loved, and I wondered that any should choose to labour on that bare mountan-side. And I saw upon the foreheads of the men as they worked a light, and the drops which fell from them as they worked had light.

And I asked God what they were seeking for.

And God touched my eyes, and I saw that what they found were small stones, which had been too bright for me to see before; and I saw that the light of the stones and the light of the men's foreheads was the same. And I saw that when one found a stone he passed it on to his fellow, and he to another, and he to another. No man kept the stone he found. And at times they gathered in great company about when a large stone was found, and raised a great shout so that the sky rang; then they worked on again.

And I asked God what they did with the stones they found at last. Then God touched my eyes again to make them stronger; and I looked, and at my very feet was a mighty crown. The light streamed out from it.

God said, "Each stone as they find it is set here."

And the crown was wrought according to a marvellous pattern; one pattern ran through all, yet each part was different.

I said to God, "How does each man know where to set his stone, so that the pattern is worked out?"

God said, "Because in the light his forehead sheds each man sees faintly outlined that full crown."

And I said, "But how is it that each stone is joined along its edges to its fellows, so that there is no seam anywhere?"

God said, "The stones are alive; they grow."

And I said, "But what does each man gain by his working?"

God said, "He sees his outline filled."

I said, "But those stones which are last set cover those which were first, and those will again be covered by those which come later."

God said, "They are covered, but not hid. The light is the light of all. Without the first, no last."

And I said to God, "When will this crown be ended?"

And God said, 'Look up!"

I looked up; and I saw the mountain tower above me, but its summit I could not see; it was lost in the clouds.

God said no more.

And I looked at the crown: then a longing seized me. Like the passion of a mother for the child whom death has taken; like the yearning of a friend for the friend whom life has buried; like the hunger of dying eyes for a life that is slipping; like the thirst of a soul for love at its first spring waking, so, but fiercer was the longing in me.

I cried to God, "I too will work here; I too will set stones in the wonderful pattern; it shall grow beneath *my* hand. And if it be that, labouring here for years, I should not find one stone, at least I will be with the men that labour here. I shall hear their shout of joy when each stone is found; I shall join in their triumph; I shall shout among them; I shall see the crown grow." So great was my longing as I looked at the crown, I thought a faint light fell from my forehead also.

God said, "Do you not hear the singing in the gardens?"

I said, "No, I hear nothing; I see only the crown." And I was dumb with longing; I forgot all the flowers of the lower Heaven and the singing there. And I ran forward, and threw my mantle on the earth and bent to seize one of the mighty tools which lay there. I could not lift it from the earth.

God said, "Where hast *thou* earned the strength to raise it? Take up thy mantle."

And I took up my mantle and followed where God called me;

but I looked back and I saw the crown burning, my crown that I had loved.

Higher and higher we climbed, and the air grew thinner. Not a tree or plant was on the bare rocks, and the stillness was unbroken. My breath came hard and quick, and the blood crept within my finger-tips. I said to God, "Is this Heaven?"

God said, "Yes; it is the highest."

And still we climbed. I said to God, "I cannot breathe so high."

God said, "Because the air is pure?"

And my head grew dizzy, and as I climbed the blood burst from my finger-tips.

Then we came out upon a lonely mountain-top.

No living being moved there; but far off on a solitary peak I saw a lonely figure standing. Whether it were man or woman I could not tell; for partly it seemed the figure of a woman, but its limbs were the mighty limbs of a man. I asked God whether it was man or woman.

God said, "In the least Heaven sex reigns supreme; in the higher it is not noticed; but in the highest it does not exist."

And I saw the figure bent over its work, and labour mightily, but what it laboured at I could not see.

I said to God, "How came it here?"

God said, "By a bloody stair. Step by step it mounted from the lowest Hell, and day by day as Hell grew farther and Heaven no nearer, it hung alone between two worlds. Hour by hour in that bitter struggle its limbs grew larger, till there fell from it rag by rag the garments which it started with. Drops fell from its eyes as it strained them; each step it climbed was wet with blood. Then it came out here."

And I thought of the garden where men sang with their arms around one another; and the mountain-side where they worked in company. And I shuddered.

And I said, "Is it not terribly alone here?"

God said, "It is never alone!"

I said, "What has it for all its labour? I see nothing return to it."

Then God touched my eyes, and I saw stretched out beneath us the plains of Heaven and Hell, and all that was within them.

God said, "From that lone height on which he stands, all things are open. To him is clear the shining in the garden, he sees the flower break forth and the streams sparkle; no shout is raised upon the mountain-side but his ear may hear it. He sees the crown grow and the light shoot from it. All Hell is open to him. He sees the paths mount upwards. To him, Hell is the seed ground from which Heaven springs. He sees the sap ascending."

And I saw the figure bend over its work, and the light from its face fell upon it.

And I said to God, "What is it making?"

And God said, "Music!"

And he touched my ears, and I heard it.

And after a long while I whispered to God, "This is Heaven."

And God asked me why I was crying. But I could not answer for joy.

And the face turned from its work, and the light fell upon me. Then it grew so bright I could not see things separately; and which were God, or the man, or I, I could not tell; we were all blended. I cried to God, "Where are you?" but there was no answer, only music and light.

Afterwards, when it had grown so dark again that I could see things separately, I found that I was standing there wrapped tight in my little old, brown, earthly cloak, and God and the man were separated from each other, and from me.

I did not dare say I would go and make music beside the man. I knew I could not reach even to his knee, nor move the instrument he played. But I thought I would stand there on my little peak and sing an accompaniment to that great music. And I tried;

but my voice failed. It piped and quavered. I could not sing that tune. I was silent.

Then God pointed to me, that I should go out of Heaven.

And I cried to God, "Oh, let me stay here! If indeed it be, as I know it is, that I am not great enough to sing upon the mountain, nor strong enough to labour on its side, nor bright enough to shine and love within the garden, at least let me go down to the great gateway; humbly I will kneel there sweeping; and, as the saved pass in, I will see the light upon their faces. I shall hear the singing in the garden, and the shout upon the hillside—"

God said, "It may not be"; he pointed.

And I cried, "If I may not stay in Heaven, then let me go down to Hell, and I will grasp the hands of men and women there; and slowly, holding one another's hands, we will work our way upwards."

Still God pointed.

And I threw myself upon the earth and cried, "Earth is so small, so mean! It is not meet a soul should see Heaven and be cast out again!"

And God laid his hand one me, and said, "Go back to earth: *That which you seek is there.*"   133–180

The Hunter

In certain valleys there was a hunter. Day by day he went to hunt for wild-fowl in the woods; and it chanced that once he stood on the shores of a large lake. While he stood waiting in the rushes for the coming of the birds, a great shadow fell on him, and in the water he saw a reflection. He looked up to the sky; but the thing was gone. Then a burning desire came over him to see once again that reflection in the water, and all day he watched and waited; but night came, and it had not returned. Then he went home with his empty bag, moody and silent. His comrades came questioning about him to know the reason, but he answered them nothing; he sat alone and brooded. Then his friend came to him, and to him he spoke.

"I have seen to-day," he said, "that which I never saw before —a vast white bird, with silver wings outstretched, sailing in the everlasting blue. And now it is as though a great fire burnt within my breast. It was but a sheen, a shimmer, a reflection in the water; but now I desire nothing more on earth than to hold her."

His friend laughed.

"It was but a beam playing on the water, or the shadow of your own head. To-morrow you will forget her," he said.

But to-morrow, and to-morrow, and to-morrow the hunter walked alone. He sought in the forest and in the woods, by the lakes and among the rushes, but he could not find her. He shot no more wild-fowl; what were they to him?

"What ails him?" said his comrades.

"He is mad," said one.

"No, but he is worse," said another, "he would see that which none of us have seen, and make himself a wonder."

"Come, let us forswear his company," said all.

So the hunter walked alone.

One night, as he wandered in the shade, very heart-sore and weeping, an old man stood before him, grander and taller than the sons of men.

"Who are you?" asked the hunter.

"I am Wisdom," answered the old man; "but some men called me Knowledge. All my life I have grown in these valleys; but no man sees me till he has sorrowed much. The eyes must be washed with tears that are to behold me; and, according as a man has suffered, I speak."

And the hunter cried—

"Oh, you who have lived here so long, tell me, what is that

great wild bird I have seen sailing in the blue? They would have me believe she is a dream; the shadow of my own head."

The old man smiled.

"Her name is Truth. He who has once seen her never rests again. Till death he desires her."

And the hunter cried—

"Oh, tell me where I may find her."

But the man said,

"You have not suffered enough," and went.

Then the hunter took from his breast the shuttle of Imagination, and wound on it the thread of his Wishes; and all night he sat and wove a net.

In the morning he spread the golden net open on the ground, and into it he threw a few grains of credulity, which his father had left him, and which he kept in his breast-pocket. They were like white puff-balls, and when you trod on them a brown dust flew out. Then he sat by to see what would happen. The first that came into the net was a snow-white bird, with dove's eyes, and he sang a beautiful song—"A human-God! a human-God! a human-God!" it sang. The second that came was black and mystical, with dark, lovely eyes, that looked into the depths of your soul, and he sang only this—"Immortality!"

And the hunter took them both in his arms, for he said—

"They are surely of the beautiful family of Truth."

Then came another, green and gold, who sang in a shrill voice, like one crying in the market-place,—"Reward after Death! Reward after Death!"

And he said—

"You are not so fair; but you are fair too," and he took it.

And others came, brightly coloured, singing pleasant songs, till all the grains were finished. And the hunter gathered all his birds together, and built a strong iron cage called a new creed, and put all his birds in it.

Then the people came about dancing and singing.

"Oh, happy hunter!" they cried. "Oh, wonderful man! Oh, delightful birds! Oh, lovely songs!"

No one asked where the birds had come from, nor how they had been caught; but they danced and sang before them. And the hunter too was glad, for he said—

"Surely Truth is among them. In time she will moult her feathers, and I shall see her snow-white form."

But the time passed, and the people sang and danced; but the hunter's heart grew heavy. He crept alone, as of old, to weep; the terrible desire had awakened again in his breast. One day, as he sat alone weeping, it chanced that Wisdom met him. He told the old man what he had done.

And Wisdom smiled sadly.

"Many men," he said, "have spread that net for Truth; but they have never found her. On the grains of credulity she will not feed; in the net of wishes her feet cannot be held; in the air of these valleys she will not breathe. The birds you have caught are of the brood of Lies. Lovely and beautiful, but still lies; Truth knows them not."

And the hunter cried out in bitterness—

"And must I then sit still to be devoured of this great burning?"

And the old man said—

"Listen, and in that you have suffered much and wept much, I will tell you what I know. He who sets out to search for Truth must leave these valleys of superstition for ever, taking with him not one shred that has belonged to them. Alone he must wander down into the Land of Absolute Negation and Denial; he must abide there; he must resist temptation; when the light breaks he must arise and follow it into the country of dry sunshine. The mountains of stern reality will arise before him; he must climb them; *beyond* them lies Truth."

"And he will hold her fast! he will hold her in his hands!" the hunter cried.

Wisdom shook his head.

"He will never see her, never hold her. The time is not yet."

"Then there is no hope?" cried the hunter.

"There is this," said Wisdom. "Some men have climbed on those mountains; circle above circle of bare rock they have scaled; and, wandering there, in those high regions, some have chanced to pick up on the ground, one white, silver feather dropped from the wing of Truth. And it shall come to pass," said the old man, raising himself prophetically and pointing with his finger to the sky, "it shall come to pass, that, when enough of those silver feathers shall have been gathered by the hands of men, and shall have been woven into a cord, and the cord into a net, that in *that* net Truth may be captured. *Nothing but Truth can hold Truth.*"

The hunter arose. "I will go," he said.

But Wisdom detained him.

"Mark you well—who leaves these valleys *never* returns to them. Though he should weep tears of blood seven days and nights upon the confines, he can never put his foot across them. Left—they are left for ever. Upon the road which you would travel there is no reward offered. Who goes, goes freely—for the great love that is in him. The work is his reward."

"I go," said the hunter; "but upon the mountains, tell me, which path shall I take?"

"I am the child of The-Accumulated-Knowledge-of-Ages," said the man; "I can walk only where many men have trodden. On these mountains few feet have passed; each man strikes out a path for himself. He goes at his own peril: my voice he hears no more. I may follow after, but I cannot go before him."

Then Knowledge vanished.

And the hunter turned. He went to his cage, and with his hands broke down the bars, and the jagged iron tore his flesh. It is sometimes easier to build than to break.

One by one he took his plumed birds and let them fly. But, when he came to his dark-plumed bird, he held it, and looked into its beautiful eyes, and the bird uttered its low deep cry—"Immortality!"

And he said quickly, "I cannot part with it. It is not heavy; it eats no food. I will hide it in my breast: I will take it with me." And he buried it there, and covered it over with his cloak.

But the thing he had hidden grew heavier, heavier, heavier—till it lay on his breast like lead. He could not move with it. He could not leave those valleys with it. Then again he took it out and looked at it.

"Oh, my beautiful, my heart's own!" he cried, "may I not keep you?"

He opened his hands sadly.

"Go," he said. "It may happen that in Truth's song one note is like to yours; but *I* shall never hear it."

Sadly he opened his hand, and the bird flew from him for ever.

Then from the shuttle of Imagination he took the thread of his wishes, and threw it on the ground; and the empty shuttle he put into his breast, for the thread was made in those valleys, but the shuttle came from an unknown country. He turned to go, but now the people came about him, howling.

"Fool, hound, demented lunatic!" they cried. "How dared you break your cage and let the birds fly?"

The hunter spoke; but they would not hear him.

"Truth! who is she? Can you eat her? can you drink her? Who has ever seen her? Your birds were real: all could hear them sing! Oh, fool! vile reptile! atheist!" they cried, "you pollute the air."

"Come, let us take up stones and stone him," cried some.

"What affair is it of ours?" said others. "Let the idiot go"; and went away. But the rest gathered up stones and mud and threw at him. At last, when he was bruised and cut, the hunter crept away into the woods. And it was evening about him.

He wandered on and on, and the shade grew deeper. He was

on the borders now of the land where it is always night. Then he stepped into it, and there was no light there. With his hands he groped; but each branch as he touched it broke off, and the earth was covered with cinders. At every step his foot sank in, and a fine cloud of impalpable ashes flew up into his face; and it was dark. So he sat down upon a stone and buried his face in his hands, to wait in that Land of Negation and Denial till the light came.

And it was night in his heart also.

Then from the marshes to his right and left cold mists arose and closed about him. A fine, imperceptible rain fell in the dark, and great drops gathered on his hair and clothes. His heart beat slowly, and a numbness crept through all his limbs. Then, looking up, two merry wisp lights came dancing. He lifted his head to look at them. Nearer, nearer they came. So warm, so bright, they danced like stars of fire. They stood before him at last. From the centre of the radiating flame in one looked out a woman's face, laughing, dimpled, with streaming yellow hair. In the centre of the other were merry laughing ripples, like the bubbles on a glass of wine. They danced before him.

"Who are you," asked the hunter, "who alone come to me in my solitude and darkness?"

"We are the twins Sensuality," they cried. "Our father's name is Human-Nature, and our mother's name is Excess. We are as old as the hills and rivers, as old as the first man; but we never die," they laughed.

"Oh, let me wrap my arms about you!" cried the first; "they are soft and warm. Your heart is frozen now, but I will make it beat. Oh, come to me!"

"I will pour my hot life into you," said the second; "your brain is numb, and your limbs are dead now; but they shall live with a fierce free life. Oh, let me pour it in!"

"Oh, follow us," they cried, "and live with us. Nobler hearts than yours have sat here in this darkness to wait, and they have come to us and we to them; and they have never left us, never. All else is a delusion, but *we* are real, we are real. Truth is a shadow; the valleys of superstition are a farce; the earth is of ashes, the trees all rotten; but we—feel us—we live! You cannot doubt us. Feel us, how warm we are! Oh, come to us! Come with us!"

Nearer and nearer round his head they hovered, and the cold drops melted on his forehead. The bright light shot into his eyes, dazzling him, and the frozen blood began to run. And he said—

"Yes; why should I die here in this awful darkness? They are warm, they melt my frozen blood!" and he stretched out his hands to take them.

Then in a moment there arose before him the image of the thing he had loved, and his hand dropped to his side.

"Oh, come to us!" they cried.

But he buried his face.

"You dazzle my eyes," he cried, "you make my heart warm; but you cannot give me what I desire. I will wait here—wait till I die. Go!"

He covered his face with his hands and would not listen; and when he looked up again they were two twinkling stars, that vanished in the distance.

And the long, long night rolled on.

All who leave the valley of superstition pass through that dark land; but some go through it in a few days, some linger there for months, some for years, and some die there.

At last for the hunter a faint light played along the horizon, and he rose to follow it; and he reached that light at last, and stepped into the broad sunshine. Then before him rose the almighty mountains of Dry-facts and Realities. The clear sunshine played on them, and the tops were lost in the clouds. At the foot many paths ran up. An exultant cry burst from the hunter. He chose the straightest and began to climb; and the rocks and ridges resounded with his song. They had exaggerated; after all, it was not so high, nor was the road so steep! A few days, a few weeks, a few months at most, and then the top! Not one feather only would he pick up; he would gather all that other men had found—weave the net—capture Truth—hold her fast—touch her with his hands —clasp her!

He laughed in the merry sunshine, and sang loud. Victory was very near. Nevertheless, after a while the path grew steeper. He needed all his breath for climbing, and the singing died away. On the right and left rose huge rocks, devoid of lichen or moss, and in the lava-like earth chasms yawned. Here and there he saw a sheen of white bones. Now too the path began to grow less and less marked; then it became a mere trace, with a foot-mark here and there; then it ceased altogether. He sang no more, but struck forth a path for himself, until he reached a mighty wall of rock, smooth and without break, stretching as far as the eye could see. "I will rear a stair against it; and, once this wall climbed, I shall be almost there," he said bravely; and worked. With his shuttle of imagination he dug out stones; but half of them would not fit, and half a month's work would roll down because those below were ill chosen. But the hunter worked on, saying always to himself, "Once this wall climbed, I shall be almost there. This great work ended!"

At last he came out upon the top, and looked about him. Far below rolled the white mist over the valleys of superstition, and above him towered the mountains. They had seemed low before; they were of an immeasurable height now, from crown to foundation surrounded by walls of rock, that rose tier above tier in mighty circles. Upon them played the eternal sunshine. He uttered a wild cry. He bowed himself on to the earth, and when he rose his face was white. In absolute silence he walked on. He was very silent now. In those high regions the rarefied air is hard to breathe by those born in the valleys; every breath he drew hurt him, and the blood oozed out from the tips of his fingers. Before the next wall of rock he began to work. The height of this seemed infinite, and he said nothing. The sound of his tool rang night and day upon the iron rocks into which he cut steps. Years passed over him, yet he worked on; but the wall towered up always above him to heaven. Sometimes he prayed that a little moss or lichen might spring up on those bare walls to be a companion to him; but it never came.

And the years rolled on: he counted them by the steps he had cut—a few for a year—only a few. He sang no more; he said no more, "I will do this or that"—he only worked. And at night, when the twilight settled down, there looked out at him from the holes and crevices in the rocks strange wild faces.

"Stop your work, you lonely man, and speak to us," they cried.

"My salvation is in work. If I should stop but for one moment you would creep down upon me," he replied. And they put out their long necks further.

"Look down into the crevice at your feet," they said. "See what lie there—white bones! As brave and strong a man as you climbed to these rocks. And he looked up. He saw there was no use in striving; he would never hold Truth, never see her, never find her. So he lay down here, for he was very tired. He went to sleep for ever. He put himself to sleep. Sleep is very tranquil. You are not lonely when you are asleep, neither do your hands ache, nor your heart." And the hunter laughed between his teeth.

"Have I torn from my heart all that was dearest; have I wandered alone in the land of night; have I resisted temptation; have I dwelt where the voice of my kind is never heard, and laboured alone, to lie down and be food for you, ye harpies?"

He laughed fiercely; and the Echoes of Despair slunk away, for the laugh of a brave, strong heart is as a death-blow to them.

Nevertheless they crept out again and looked at him.

"Do you know that your hair is white?" they said, "that your hands begin to tremble like a child's? Do you see that the point of your shuttle is gone?—it is cracked already. If you should ever climb this stair," they said, "it will be your last. You will never climb another."

And he answered, "*I know it!*" and worked on.

The old, thin hands cut the stones ill and jaggedly, for the fingers were stiff and bent. The beauty and the strength of the man was gone.

At last, an old, wizened, shrunken face looked out above the rocks. It saw the eternal mountains rise with walls to the white clouds; but its work was done.

The old hunter folded his tired hands and lay down by the precipice where he had worked away his life. It was the sleeping time at last. Below him over the valleys rolled the thick white mist. Once it broke; and through the gap the dying eyes looked down on the trees and fields of their childhood. From afar seemed borne to him the cry of his own wild birds, and he heard the noise of people singing as they danced. And he thought he heard among them the voices of his old comrades; and he saw far off the sunlight shine on his early home. And great tears gathered in the hunter's eyes.

"Ah! they who die there do not die alone," he cried.

Then the mists rolled together again; and he turned his eyes away.

"I have sought," he said, "for long years I have laboured; but I have not found her. I have not rested, I have not repined, and I have not seen her; now my strength is gone. Where I lie down worn out, other men will stand, young and fresh. By the steps that I have cut they will climb; by the stairs that I have built, they will mount. They will never know the name of the man who made them. At the clumsy work they will laugh; when the stones roll they will curse me. But they will mount, and on *my* work; they will climb, and by *my* stair! They will find her, and through me! And no man liveth to himself, and no man dieth to himself."

The tears rolled from beneath the shrivelled eyelids. If Truth had appeared above him in the clouds now he could not have seen her, the mist of death was in his eyes.

"My soul hears their glad step coming," he said; "and they shall mount! they shall mount!" He raised his shrivelled hand to his eyes.

Then slowly from the white sky above, through the still air, came something falling, falling, falling. Softly it fluttered down, and dropped on to the breast of the dying man. He felt it with his hands. It was a feather. He died holding it. 25-50

Woman and Labor

$\mathcal{T}$he women of no race or class will ever rise in revolt or attempt to bring about a revolutionary readjustment of their relation to their society, however intense their suffering and however clear their perception of it, while the welfare and persistence of their society requires their submission: that, wherever there is a general attempt on the part of the women of any society to readjust their position in it, a close analysis will always show that the changed or changing conditions of that society have made woman's acquiescence no longer necessary or desirable. 6–7

Already throughout the modern civilized world we have reached a point at which the social demand is not merely for human creatures in the bulk for use as beasts of burden, but, rather, and only, for such human creatures as shall be so trained and cultured as to be fitted for the performance of the more complex duties of modern life. Not, now, merely for many men, but, rather, for few men, and those few, well-born and well-instructed, is the modern demand. And the woman who to-day merely produces twelve children and suckles them, and then turns them loose on her society and family, is regarded, and rightly so, as a curse and down-draft, and not the productive laborer, of her community. Indeed, so difficult and expensive has become in the modern world the rearing and training of even one individual, in a manner suited to fit it for coping with the complexities and difficulties of civilized life, that, to the family as well as to the state, unlimited fecundity on the part of the female has already, in most cases, become an irremediable evil. It is thus in the case of the artisan, who at the cost of immense self-sacrifice must support and train his children till their twelfth or fourteenth year, if they are ever to become even skilled manual laborers, and who if his family be large often sinks beneath the burden, allowing his offspring, untaught and untrained, to become waste products of human life. So with the professional man, who by his mental toil is compelled to support and educate, at immense expense, his sons till they are twenty or older, and to sustain his daughters, often throughout their whole lives should they not marry, and to whom a large family proves often no less disastrous; while the state whose women produce recklessly large masses of individuals in excess of those for whom they can provide instruction and nourishment is a state, in so far, tending toward deterioration.   58–59

There is, indeed, often something pathetic in the attitude of many a good old mother of the race, who having survived, here and there, into the heart of our modern civilization, is sorely puzzled by the change in woman's duties and obligations. She may be found looking into the eyes of some ancient crone, who, like herself, has survived from a previous state of civilization, seeking there a confirmation of a view of life of which a troublous doubt has crept even into her own soul. "I," she cries, "always cured my own hams, and knitted my own socks, and made up all the linen by hand. We always did it when we were girls—but now my daughters object!" And her old crone answers her: "Yes, we did it; it's the right thing; but it's so expensive. It's so much cheaper to buy things ready made!" And they shake their heads and go their ways, feeling that the world is strangely out of joint when duty seems no more duty. Such women are, in truth, like a good old mother duck, who, having for years led her ducklings to the same pond, when that pond has been drained and nothing is left but baked mud, will still persist in bringing her younglings

down to it, and walks about with flapping wings and anxious quack, trying to induce them to enter it. But the ducklings, with fresh young instincts, hear far off the delicious drippings from the new dam which has been built higher up to catch the water, and they smell the chickweed and the long grass that is growing up beside it; and absolutely refuse to disport themselves on the baked mud and to pretend to seek for worms where no worms are. And they leave the ancient mother quacking beside her pond and set out to seek for new pastures—perhaps to lose themselves upon the way? perhaps to find them? To the old mother one is inclined to say, "Ah good old mother duck, can you not see the world has changed? You cannot bring the water back into the dried-up pond! Mayhap it was better and pleasanter when it was there, but it has gone for ever; and, would you and yours swim again, it must be in other waters." New machinery, new duties.
   49–50[Footnote]

A horseman, riding along on a dark night in an unknown land, may chance to feel his horse start beneath him; rearing, it may almost hurl him to the earth: in the darkness he may curse his beast, and believe its aim is simply to cast him off, and free itself for ever of its burden. But when the morning dawns and lights the hills and valleys he has traveled, looking backward, he may perceive that the spot where his beast reared, planting its feet into the earth, and where it refused to move farther on the old road, was indeed the edge of a mighty precipice, down which one step more would have precipitated both horse and rider. And he may then see that it was an instinct wiser than his own which led his creature, though in the dark, to leap backward, seeking a new path along which both might travel.
   In the confusion and darkness of the present, it may well seem to some that woman, in her desire to seek for new paths of labor and employment, is guided only by an irresponsible impulse; or

that she seeks selfishly only her own good, at the cost of that of the race, which she has so long and faithfully borne onward. But, when a clearer future shall have arisen and the obscuring mists of the present have been dissipated, may it not then be clearly manifest that not for herself alone, but for her entire race, has woman sought her new paths?   71–72

The males of the dominant class have almost always contrived to absorb to themselves the new intellectual occupations, which the absence of necessity for the old forms of physical toil made possible in their societies; and the females of the dominant class or race, for whose muscular labors there was now also no longer any need, not succeeding in grasping or attaining to these new forms of labor, have sunk into a state in which, performing no species of active social duty, they have existed through the passive performance of sexual functions alone, with how much or how little of discontent will now never be known, since no literary record has been made by the woman of the past, of her desires or sorrows. Then, in place of the active laboring woman, upholding society by her toil, has come the effete wife, concubine or prostitute, clad in fine raiment, the work of others' fingers; fed on luxurious viands, the result of others' toil, waited on and tended by the labor of others. The need for her physical labor having gone, and mental industry not having taken its place, she bedecked and scented her person, or had it bedecked and scented for her, she lay upon her sofa, or drove or was carried out in her vehicle, and, loaded with jewels, she sought by dissipations and amusements to fill up the inordinate blank left by the lack of productive activity. And the hand whitened and frame softened, till, at last, the very duties of motherhood, which were all the consitution of her life left her, became distasteful, and, from the instant when her infant came damp from her womb, it passed into the hands of others, to be tended and reared by them; and from youth to age her offspring often owed nothing to her personal toil. In many cases so complete was her enervation, that at last the very joy of giving life, the glory and beatitude of a virile womanhood, became distasteful; and she sought to evade it, not because of its interference with more imperious duties to those already born of her, or to her society, but because her existence of inactivity had robbed her of all joy in strenuous exertion and endurance in any form. Finely clad, tenderly housed, life became for her merely the gratification of her own physical and sexual appetites, and the appetites of the male, through the stimulation of which she could maintain herself. And, whether as kept wife, kept mistress, or prostitute, she contributed nothing to the active and sustaining labors of her society. 79–81

Among the Jews in the days of their health and growth, we find their women bearing the major weight of agricultural and domestic toil, full always of labor and care—from Rachel, whom Jacob met and loved as she watered her father's flocks, to Ruth, the ancestress of a line of kings and heroes, whom her Boas noted laboring in the harvest-fields; from Sarah, kneading and baking cakes for Abraham's prophetic visitors, to Miriam, prophetess and singer, and Deborah, who judged Israel from beneath her palm-tree, "and the land had rest for forty years." Everywhere the ancient Jewish woman appears an active sustaining power among her people; and perhaps the noblest picture of the laboring woman to be found in any literature is contained in the Jewish writings, indited possibly at the very time when the laboring woman was for the first time tending among a section of the Jews to become a thing of the past; when already Solomon, with his seven hundred parasitic wives and three hundred parasitic concubines, loomed large on the horizon of the national life, to take the place of flock-tending Rachel and gleaning Ruth, and to produce amid their palaces of cedar and gold, among them all, no Joseph or David, but in the way of descendant only a Rehoboam, under whose hand the kingdom was to totter to its fall.   94–97

If woman is content to leave to the male all labor in the new and all-important fields which are rapidly opening before the human race; if, as the old forms of domestic labor slip from her for ever and inevitably, she does not grasp the new, it is inevitable, that, ultimately, not merely a class, but the whole bodies of females in civilized societies, must sink into a state of more or less absolute dependence on their sexual functions alone.

As new forms of natural force are mastered and mechanical appliances perfected, it will be quite possible for the male half of all civilized races (and therefore ultimately of all) to absorb the entire fields of intellectual and highly trained manual labor; and it would be entirely possible for the female half of the race, whether as prostitutes, as kept mistresses, or as kept wives, to cease from all forms of active toil, and, as the passive tools of sexual reproduction, or, more decadently still, as the mere instruments of sexual indulgence, to sink into a condition of complete and helpless sex-parasitism.   115–117

The truth that, as the first primitive human males and females, unable to count farther than their fingers, or grasp an abstract idea, or feel the controlling power of social emotion, could only develop into the Sapphos, Aristotles, and Shelleys of a more expanded civilization, if side by side, and line by line, male and female forms have expanded together, if, as the convolutions of his brain increased in complexity, so increased the convolutions of hers; if, as her forehead grew higher, so developed his; and that, if the long upward march of the future is ever to be accomplished by the race, male and female must march side by side, acting and reacting on each other through inheritance; or progress is impossible. The truth that, as the existence of even the male Bushman would be impossible without the existence of the analogous Bush-woman, with the same gifts, and that races which can produce among their males a William Kingdon Clifford, a Tolstoy, or a Robert Browning, would be inconceivable and impossible, unless among its females it could also produce a Sophia Kovalevsky, a George Eliot, or a Louise Michel, so, in the future, that higher and more socialized human race we dream of can only come into existence, because both the sex forms have evolved together, now this sex and then that, so to speak, catching up the ball of life and throwing it back to the other, slightly if imperceptibly enlarging and beautifying it as it passes through their hands. Without the reaction of interevolution between the sexes, there can be no real and permanent human advance. . . .   132–133

The artificial social movements which have had their origin in the arbitrary will of individuals, guided with however much determination and reason, have of necessity proved ephemeral and abortive. An Alexander might will to weld a Greece and an Asia into one; a Napoleon might resolve to create of a diversified Europe one consolidated state; and by dint of skill and determination they might for a moment appear to be accomplishing that which they desired; but the constraining individual will being withdrawn, the object of their toils has melted away, as the little heap of damp sand gathered under the palm of a child's hand on the sea-shore melts away, scattered by the wind and washed out by the waves, the moment the hand that shaped it is withdrawn; while the small, soft, indefinite, watery fragment of jelly-fish lying beside it, though tossed hither and thither by water and wind, yet retains its shape and grows, because its particles are bound by an internal and organic force.   137–138

He who to-day looks at some great Gothic cathedral in its final form, seems to be looking at that which might have been the incarnation of the dream of some single soul of genius. But in truth, its origin was far otherwise. Ages elapsed from the time the first rough stone was laid as a foundation till the last spire and pinnacle were shaped, and the hand which laid the foundation-stone was never the same as that which set the last stone upon the coping. Generations often succeeded one another, laboring at gargoyle, rose-window, and shaft, and died, leaving the work to others; the master-builder who drew up the first rough outline passed away, and was succeeded by others, and the details of the work as completed bore sometimes but faint resemblance to the work as he devised it; no man fully understood all that others had done or were doing, but each labored in his place; and the work as completed had unity; it expressed not the desire and necessity of one mind, but of the human spirit of that age; and not less essential to the existence of the building was the labor of the workman who passed a life of devotion in carving gargoyles or shaping rose-windows, than that of the greatest master who drew general outlines: perhaps it was yet more heroic; because, for the master-builder, who, even if but vaguely, has an image of what the work would be when the last stone was laid and the last spire raised, it was easy to labor with devotion and zeal, though well he might know that the placing of that last stone and the raising of that last spire would not be his, and that the building in its full beauty and strength he should never see; but for the journeyman laborer who carried on his duties and month by month toiled at carving his own little gargoyle or shaping the traceries in his own little oriel window, without any complete vision, it was not so easy; nevertheless, it was through the conscientious labors of such alone, through their heaps of chipped and spoiled stones, which may have lain thick about them, that at the last the pile was reared in its strength and beauty. 142–144

It is often said of those who lead in this attempt at the readaption of woman's relation to life, that they are "New Women"; and they are at times spoken of as though they were a something portentous and unheard-of in the order of human life. But, the truth is, we are not new. We who lead in this movement to-day are of that old, old Teutonic womanhood, which twenty centuries ago plowed its march through European forests and morasses beside its male companion; which marched with the Cimbri to Italy, and with the Franks across the Rhine, with the Varagians into Russia, and the Alamani into Switzerland; which peopled Scandinavia, and penetrated to Britain; whose priestesses had their shrines in German forests, and gave out the oracle for peace or war. We have in us the blood of a womanhood that was never bought and never sold; that wore no veil, and had no foot bound; whose realized ideal of marriage was sexual companionship and an equality in duty and labor; who stood side by side with the males they loved in peace or war, and whose children, when they had borne them, sucked manhood from their breasts, and even through their fetal existence heard a brave heart beat above them. We are women of a breed whose racial ideal was no Helen of Troy, passed passively from male hand to male hand, as men pass gold or lead; but that Brynhild whom Segurd found, clad in helm and byrnie, the warrior maid, who gave him counsel, "the deepest that ever yet was given to living man," and "wrought on him to the performing of great deeds"; who, when he died, raised high the funeral pyre and lay down on it beside him, crying, "Nor shall the door swing to at the heel of him as I go in beside him!" We are of a race of women that of old knew no fear, and feared no death; and if to-day some of us have fallen on evil and degenerate times, there moves in us yet the throb of the old blood. If it be to-day on no physical battlefield that we stand beside our men, and on no march through an external forest or morass that we have to lead; it is yet the old spirit which, undimmed by two thousands years, stirs within us in deeper and subtler ways; it is yet the cry of the old, free Northern woman which makes the world to-day. Though the battle be now for us all, in the laboratory or the workshop, in the forum or the study, in the assembly and in the mart, with the pen and not the sword, of the head and not the arm; we still stand side by side with the men we love, "to dare with them in war and to suffer with them in peace," as the Roman wrote of our old Northern womanhood.   147–149.

To insist that all Jews, and none but Jews, should lead and instruct in religious matters; that all Englishmen, and none but Englishmen, should engage in trade; that each German should make his living by music, and none but a German allowed to practise it, would drive to despair the unfortunate individual Englishman, whose most marked deficiency might be in the direction of finance and bartering trade power; the Jew, whose religious instincts might be entirely rudimentary; or the German, who could not distinguish one note from another; and the society as a whole would be an irremediable loser, in one of the heaviest of all forms of social loss—the loss of the full use of the highest capacities of all its members.   168–169

As there is no need to legislate that Hindus, being generally supposed to have a natural incapacity for field sports, shall not betake themselves to them—for, if they have no capacity, they will fail; and, as in spite of the Hindus' supposed general incapacity for sport, it is possible for an individual Hindu to become the noted batsman of his age; so, there is no need to legislate that women should be restricted in her choice of fields of labor; for the organic incapacity of the individual, if it exist, will legislate far more strongly than any artificial, legal, or social obstruction can do; and it may be that the one individual in ten thousand who selects a field not generally sought by their fellows will enrich

humanity by the result of an especial genius. Allowing all to start
from the one point in the world of intellectual culture and labor,
with our ancient Mother Nature sitting as umpire, distributing
the prizes and scratching from the lists the incompetent, is all we
demand, but we demand it determinedly. Throw the puppy into
the water: if it swims, well; if it sinks, well; but do not tie a rope
round its throat and weight it with a brick, and then assert its
incapacity to keep afloat.

For the present, *we take all labor for our province!*

From the judge's seat to the legislator's chair; from the statesman's closet to the merchant's office; from the chemist's laboratory to the astronomer's tower, there is no post or form of toil
for which it is not our intention to attempt to fit ourselves; and
there is no closed door we do not intend to force open; and there
is no fruit in the garden of knowledge it is not our determination
to eat. Acting in us, and through us, nature will mercilessly ex-
pose to us our deficiencies in the field of human toil and reveal
to us our powers. *And, for to-day, we take all labor for our province!*
171–173

"What then of war, that struggle of the human creature to attain
its ends by physical force and at the price of the life of others: will
you take part in that also?" We reply: Yes; more particularly in
that field we intend to play our part. We have always borne part
of the weight of war, and the major part. It is not that in primitive
times we suffered from the destruction of the fields we tilled and
the houses we built; it is not that later as domestic laborers and
producers, though unwaged, we, in taxes and material loss and
additional labor, paid as much as our male towards the cost of
war; it is not that in a comparatively insignificant manner, as
nurses of the wounded in modern times, or now and again as
warrior chieftainesses and leaders in primitive and other societies, we have borne our part; nor is it even because the spirit of

resolution in its women, and their willingness to endure, has in all ages, again and again largely determined the fate of a race that goes to war, that we demand our controlling right where war is concerned. Our relation to war is far more intimate, personal, and indissoluble than this. Men have made boomerangs, bows, swords, or guns with which to destroy one another; we have made the men who destroyed and were destroyed! We have in all ages produced, at an enormous cost, the primal munition of war, without which no other would exist. There is no battlefield on earth, nor ever has been, howsoever covered with slain, which it has not cost the women of the race more in actual bloodshed and anguish to supply, than it has cost the men who lie there. *We pay the first cost on all human life.*   173–174

There is, perhaps, no woman, whether she have borne children, or be merely potentially a child-bearer, who could look down upon a battlefield covered with slain, but the thought would rise in her, "So many mothers' sons! So many young bodies brought into the world to lie there! So many months of weariness and pain while bones and muscles were shaped within! So many hours of anguish and struggle that breath might be! So many baby mouths drawing life at women's breasts;—all this, that men might lie with glazed eyeballs, and swollen faces, and fixed, blue, unclosed mouths, and great limbs tossed—this, that an acre of ground might be manured with human flesh, that next year's grass or poppies or karoo bushes may spring up greener and redder, where they have lain, or that the sand of a plain may have a glint of white bones!" And we cry, "Without an inexorable cause, this must not be!" No woman who is a woman says of a human body, "It is nothing!"   175–176

If our European nations should continue in their present semi-civilized condition a few generations longer, it is highly probable that as financiers, as managers of the commissariat department, as inspectors of provisions and clothing for the army, women may probably play a very leading part; and that the nation which is the first to employ women may be placed at a vast advantage over its fellows in time of war. It is not because of woman's cowardice, incapacity, nor, above all, because of her general superior virtue, that she will end war when her voice is fully and clearly heard in the governance of states—it is because, on this one point, and on this point almost alone, the knowledge of woman, simply as woman, is superior to that of man; she knows the history of human flesh; she knows its cost; he does not.   178–179

In a besieged city, it might well happen that men in the streets might seize upon statues and marble carvings from public buildings and galleries and hurl them in to stop the breaches made in their ramparts by the enemy, unconsideringly and merely because they came first to hand, not valuing them more than had they been paving-stones. One man, however, could not do this —the sculptor. He, who, though there might be no work of his own chisel among them, yet knew what each of these works of art had cost, knew by experience the long years of struggle and study and the infinitude of toil which had gone to the shaping of even one limb, to the carving of even one perfected outline, he could never so use them without thought or care. Instinctively he would seek to throw in household goods, even gold and silver, all the city held, before he sacrificed its works of art!

Men's bodies are our woman's works of art. Given to us power to control, we will never carelessly throw them in to fill up the gaps in human relationships made by international ambitions and greeds. The thought would never come to us as women, "Cast in men's bodies; settle the thing so!" Arbitration and compensation would as naturally occur to her as cheaper and simpler methods of bridging the gaps in national relationships, as to the

sculptor it would occur to throw in anything rather than statuary,
though he might be driven to that at last!   179–180

The physical creation of human life, which, in as far as the male
is concerned, consists in a few moments of physical pleasure, to
the female must always signify months of pressure and physical
endurance, crowned with danger to life. To the male, the giving
of life is a laugh; to the female, blood, anguish, and sometimes
death. Here we touch one of the few yet important differences
between man and woman as such.

The twenty thousand men prematurely slain on a field of battle, mean, to the women of their race, twenty thousand human
creatures to be borne within them for months, given birth to in
anguish, fed from their breasts and reared with toil, if the numbers of the tribe and the strength of the nation are to be main-
tained. In nations continually at war, incessant and unbroken
child-bearing is by war imposed on all women if the state is to
survive; and whenever war occurs, if numbers are to be main-
tained, there must be an increased child-bearing and rearing.
This throws upon woman as woman a war tax, compared with
which all that the male expends in military preparations is comparatively light.   180–181

It is true that the woman will sacrifice as mercilessly, as cruelly,
the life of a hated rival or an enemy, as any male; *but she always
knows what she is doing, and the value of the life she takes!* There is no
light-hearted, careless enjoyment in the sacrifice of life to the
normal woman; her instinct, instructed by experience, steps in to
prevent it. She always knows what life costs; and that it is more
easy to destroy than create it.   182

The man and the woman alike, who with Isaiah on the hills of
Palestine, or the Indian Buddha under his bo-tree, have seen the
essential unity of all sentient life; and who therefore see in war

but a symptom of that crude disco-ordination of life on earth, not yet at one with itself, which affects humanity in these early stages of its growth; and who are compelled to regard as the ultimate goal of the race, though yet perhaps far distant across the ridges of innumerable coming ages, that harmony between all forms of conscious life, metaphorically prefigured by the ancient Hebrew, when he cried, "The wolf shall dwell with the lamb; and the leopard shall lie down with the kid; and the calf and the young lion and the fatling together, and a little child shall lead them!" —to the individual, whether man or woman, who has reached this standpoint, there is no need for enlightenment from the instincts of the child-bearers of society as such; their condemnation of war, rising not so much from the fact that it is a wasteful destruction of human flesh, as that it is an indication of the non-existence of that co-ordination, the harmony which is summed up in the cry, "My little children, love one another."   182–183

It is especially in the domain of war that we, the bearers of men's bodies, who supply its most valuable munition, who, not amid the clamor and ardor of battle, but singly, and alone, with a three-in-the-morning courage, shed our blood and face death that the battlefield might have its food, a food more precious to us than our heart's blood; it is we especially who, in the domain of war, have our word to say, a word no man can say for us. It is our intention to enter into the domain of war and to labor there till in the course of generations we have extinguished it.   184

We, to-day, take all labor for our province! We seek to enter the non-sexual fields of intellectual or physical toil, because we are unable to see to-day, with regard to them, any dividing wall raised by sex which excludes us from them. We are yet equally determined to enter those in which sex does play its part, because it is here that woman, the bearer of the race, must stand side by side with man, the begetter; if a completed human wisdom, an insight that misses no aspect of human life, and an activity that is in harmony with the entire knowledge and the entire instinct of the human race, is to exist. It is here that the man cannot act for the woman nor the woman for the man; but both must interact. It is here that each sexual half of the race, so closely and indistinguishably blended elsewhere, has its own distinct contribution to make to the sum total of human knowledge and human wisdom. Neither is the woman without the man, nor the man without the woman, the completed human intelligence.

We claim, to-day, all labor for our province! Those large fields in which it would appear sex plays no part, and equally those in which it plays a part.   202–203

A certain mental camaraderie and community of impersonal interests is imperative in conjugal life in addition to a purely sexual relation, if the union is to remain a living and growing reality. It is more especially because the sharing by woman of the labors of man will tend to promote camaraderie and the existence of common, impersonal interests and like habits of thought and life, that the entrance of women into the fields shared by men, and not into others peculiarly reserved for her, is so desirable.[1]   294–295

1. The reply given once by the wife of a leading barrister, when reference was made to the fact that she and her husband were seldom found in each other's society, throws a painful but true light on certain aspects of modern life, against which the entire woman's movement of our age is a rebellion. "My husband," she said, "is always increasingly absorbed in his legal duties, of which I understand nothing, and which so do not interest me. My children are all growing up and at school. I have servants enough to attend to my house. When he comes home in the evening, if I try to amuse him by telling him of the things I have been doing during the day, of the bazaars I am working for, the shopping I have done, the visits I have paid, he is bored. He is anxious to get away to his study, his books, and his men friends, and I am left utterly alone. If it were not for the society of women and other men with whom I have more in common, I could not bear my life. When we first met as boy and girl, and fell in love, we danced and rode together and seemed to have everything in common; now we have nothing. I respect him and I believe he respects me, but that is all!"

Always in our dreams we hear the turn of the key that shall close the door of the last brothel; the clink of the last coin that pays for the body and soul of a woman; the falling of the last wall that encloses artificially the activity of woman and divides her from man; always we picture the love of the sexes as once a dull, slow, creeping worm; then a torpid, earthy chrysalis; at last the full-winged insect, glorious in the sunshine of the future.

To-day, as we row hard against the stream of life, is it only a blindness in our eyes, which have been too long strained, which makes us see, far up the river where it fades into the distance, through all the mists that rise from the river-banks, a clear, a golden light? Is it only a delusion of the eyes which makes us grasp our oars more lightly and bend our backs lower; though we know well that, long before the boat reaches those stretches, other hands than ours will man the oars and guide its helm? Is it all a dream?

The ancient Chaldean seer had a vision of a Garden of Eden which lay in a remote past. It was dreamed that man and woman once lived in joy and fellowship, till woman ate of the tree of knowledge and gave to man to eat; and that both were driven forth to wander, to toil in bitterness; because they had eaten of the fruit.

We also have our dream of a Garden, but it lies in a distant future. We dream that woman shall eat of the tree of knowledge together with man, and that side by side and hand close to hand, through ages of much toil and labor, they shall together raise about them an Eden nobler than any the Chaldean dreamed of; an Eden created by their own labor and made beautiful by their own fellowship.

In his apocalypse there was one who saw a new heaven and a new earth; we see a new earth; but therein dwells love—the love of comrades and co-workers.

It is because so wide and gracious to us are the possibilities of the future; so impossible is a return to the past, so deadly is a passive acquiescence in the present, that to-day we are found everywhere raising our strange new cry—"Labor and the training that fits us for labor!"   297–299

Trooper Peter Halket
of
Mashonaland

The Stranger's Company

"*W*e are the most vast of all companies on the earth," said the stranger; "and we are always growing. We have among us men of every race and from every land; the Esquimo, the Chinaman, the Turk, and the Englishman,—we have them all. We have men of every religion,—Buddhists, Mahometans, Confucians, Free-thinkers, Atheists, Christians, Jews. It matters to us nothing by what name the man is named, so he be one of us." 48–49

"They are of all races," said the stranger. "In a city in the old Colony is one of us, small of stature and small of voice. It came to pass on a certain Sunday morning, when the men and women were gathered before him, that he mounted his pulpit; and he said when the time for the sermon came, 'In place that I should speak to you, I will read you an history.' And he opened an old book more than two thousand years old, and he read:—

" 'Now it came to pass that Naboth the Jezreelite had a vineyard, which was in Jezreel, hard by the palace of Ahab king of Samaria.

" 'And Ahab spake unto Naboth, saying, Give me thy vineyard, that I may have it for a garden of herbs, because it is near unto my house: and I will give thee for it a better vineyard than it; or if it seem good to thee, I will give thee the worth of it in money.

" 'And Naboth said to Ahab, The Lord forbid it me, that I should give the inheritance of my fathers unto thee.

" 'And Ahab came into his house heavy and displeased, because of the word which Naboth the Jezreelite had spoken unto

119

him: for he had said, I will not give the inheritance of my fathers.'

"The man read the whole story until it was ended. Then he closed the book, and he said, 'My friends, Naboth has a vineyard in this land, and in it there is much gold; and Ahab has desired to have it that the wealth may be his.'

"And he put the old book aside, and he took up another which was written yesterday. And the men and women whispered one to another, even in the church, 'Is not that the Blue Book Report of the Select Committee of the Cape Parliament on the Jameson raid?'

"And the man said, 'Friends, the first story I have read you is one of the oldest stories of the world; the story I am about to read you is one of the newest. Truth is not more truth because it is three thousand years old, nor is it less truth because it is of yesterday. All books which throw light on truth are God's books, therefore I shall read to you from the pages before me. Shall the story of Ahab king of Samaria profit us when we know not the story of the Ahabs of the our day; and the Naboths of our land be stoned while we sit at ease?' And he read to them portions of that book. And certain rich men and women rose up and went out even while he spoke, and his wife also went out.

"And when the service was ended and the man returned to his home, his wife came to him weeping; and she said: 'Did you see how some of the most wealthy and important people got up and went out this morning? Why did you preach such a sermon, when we were just going to have the new wing added to our house, and you thought they were going to raise your salary? You have not a single Boer in your congregation! Why need you say the Chartered Company raid on Johannesburg was wrong?'

"He said: 'My wife, if I believe that certain men whom we have raised on high, and to whom we have given power, have done a cowardly wrong, shall I not say it?'

"And she said: 'Yes, and only a little while ago, when Rhodes was licking the dust off the Boers' feet that he might keep them from suspecting while he got ready this affair, then you attacked both Rhodes and the Bond for trying to pass a bill for flogging the niggers, and we lost fifty pounds we might have got for the church.'

"And he said: 'My wife, cannot God be worshipped as well under the dome of the heaven He made as in a golden palace? Shall a man keep silence, when he sees oppression, to earn money for God? If I have defended the black man when I believed him to be wronged, shall I not also defend the white man, my flesh-brother? Shall we speak when one man is wronged and not when it is another?'

"And she said: 'Yes, but you have your family and yourself to think of! Why are you always in oppostion to the people who could do something for us? You are only loved by the poor. If it is necessary for you to attack some one, why don't you attack the Jews for killing Christ, or Herod, or Pontius Pilate? Why don't you leave alone the men who are in power to-day, and who with their money can crush you?'

"And he said: 'Oh, my wife, those Jews and Herod and Pontius Pilate are long dead. If I should preach of them, now would it help them? Would it save one living thing from their clutches? The past is dead—it lives only for us to learn from. The present, the present only, is ours to work in, and the future ours to create. Is all the gold of Johannesburg, or are all the diamonds of Kimberley worth, that one Christian man should fall by the hand of his fellows—aye, or one heathen brother?'

"And she answered: 'Oh, that is all very well. If you were a really eloquent preacher, and could draw hundreds of men about you, and in time form a great party with you at its head, I shouldn't mind what you said. But you, with your little figure and your little voice, who will ever follow you! You will be left all alone; that is all the good that will ever come to you through it.'

"And he said: 'Oh, my wife, have I not waited and watched, and hoped that they who are nobler and stronger than I, all over this land, would lift up their voices and speak?—and there is only a deadly silence. Here and there one has dared to speak aloud, but the rest whisper behind the hand. One says, "My son has a post: he would lose it if I spoke loud"; and another says, "I have a promise of land"; and another, "I am socially intimate with these men, and should lose my social standing if I let my voice be heard." Oh, my wife, our land, our goodly land, which we had hoped would be free and strong among the peoples of earth, is rotten and honeycombed with the tyranny of gold! We, who had hoped to stand first in the Anglo-Saxon sisterhood, for justice and freedom, are not even fit to stand last. Do I not know only too bitterly how weak is my voice, and that that which I can do is as nothing? But shall I remain silent? Shall the glow-worm refuse to give its light, because it is not a star set up on high? shall the broken stick refuse to burn and warm one frozen man's hands, because it is not a beacon light flaming across the earth? Ever a voice is behind my shoulder that whispers to me: *"Why break your head against a stone wall? Leave this work to the greater and larger men of your people; they who will do it better than you can do it! Why break your heart when life could be so fair to you?"* But oh, my wife, the strong men are silent; and shall I not speak, though I know my power is as nothing?'

"He laid his head upon his hands.

"And she said, "I cannot understand you. When I come home and tell you that this man drinks, or that that woman has got into trouble, you always answer me, "Wife, what business is it of ours, if so be that we cannot help them?" A little innocent gossip offends you; and you go to visit people, and treat them as your friends, into whose house I would not go. Yet when the richest and strongest men in the land, who could crush you with their money, as a boy crushes a fly between his finger and thumb, take a certain course, you stand and oppose them.'

"And he said: 'My wife, with the sins of the private man, what have I to do, if so be I have not led him into them? Am I guilty? I have enough to do looking after my own sins. The sin that a man sins against himself is his alone, not mine; the sin that a man sins against his fellows is his and theirs, not mine; but the sins that a man sins, in that he is taken up by the hands of a people and set up on high, and whose hand they have armed with their sword, whose power to strike is their power—his sins are theirs; there is no man so small in the whole nation that he dare say, "I have no responsibility for this man's action." We armed him, we raised him, we strengthened him, and the evil he accomplishes is more ours than his. If this man's end in South Africa should be accomplished, and the day should come when, from the Zambesi to the sea, white man should fly at white man's throat, and every man's heart burn with bitterness against his fellow, and the land be bathed with blood as rain,—shall I then dare to pray, who have now feared to speak? Do not think I wish for punishment upon these men. Let them take the millions they have wrung out of this land, and go to the lands of their birth; and live in wealth, luxury, and joy; but let them leave this land they have tortured and ruined. Let them keep the money they have made here; we may be the poorer for it, but they cannot then crush our freedom with it. Shall I ask my God Sunday by Sunday to brood across the land, and bind all its children's hearts in a close-knit fellowship;—yet, when I see its people betrayed, and their jawbone broken by a stroke from the hand of gold; when I see freedom passing from us, and the whole land being grasped by the golden claw, so that the generation after us shall be born without freedom, to labor for the men who have clasped all,—shall I hold my peace? The Boer and the Englishman who have been in this land have not always loved mercy, nor have they always sought after justice; but the little finger of the speculator and monopolist who are devouring this land will be thicker on the backs of the children of this land, black and white, than the loins of the Dutchmen and Englishmen who have been.'

"And she said: 'I have heard it said that it was our duty to sacrifice ourselves for the men and women living in the world at the same time as ourselves; but I never before heard that we had to sacrifice ourselves for people that are not born. What are they to you? You will be dust, and lying in your grave, before that time comes. If you believe in God,' she said, 'why cannot you leave it to him to bring good out of all this evil? Does he need *you* to be made a martyr of? or will the world be lost without *you?*'

"He said: 'Wife, if my right hand be in a fire, shall I not pull it out? Shall I say, "God may bring good out of this evil," and let it burn? That Unknown that lies beyond us we know of no otherwise than through its manifestation in our own hearts; it works no otherwise upon the sons of men than through man. And shall I feel no bond binding me to the men to come, and desire no good or beauty for them—I, who am what I am, and enjoy what I enjoy, because for countless ages in the past men have lived and labored, who lived not for themselves alone, and counted no costs? Would the great statue, the great poem, the great reform ever be accomplished, if men counted the cost, and created for their own lives alone? And no man liveth to himself, and no man dieth to himself. You cannot tell me not to love the men who shall be after me; a soft voice within me, I know not what, cries out ever, "Live for them, as for your own children." When in the circle of my own small life all is dark and I despair, hope springs up in me when I remember that something nobler and fairer may spring up in the spot where I now stand.'

"And she said: 'You want to put every one against us! The other women will not call on me; and our church is more and more made up of poor people. Money holds by money. If your congregation were Dutchmen, I know you would be always preaching to love the Englishman, and be kind to niggers. If they were Kaffirs, you would always be telling them to help white men. You will never be on the side of the people who can do anything for us! You know the offer we had from—'

"And he said: 'Oh, my wife, what are the Boer, and the Russian, and the Turk to me? Am I responsible for their action? It is my own nation, mine, which I love as a man loves his own soul, whose acts touch me. I would that wherever our flag was planted the feeble or oppressed peoples of earth might gather under it, saying, "Under this banner is freedom and justice which knows no race or color." I wish that on our banner were blazoned in large letters *"Justice and Mercy,"* and that in every new land which our feet touch, every son among us might see ever blazoned above his head that banner, and below it the great order, *"By this sign, Conquer!"* and that the pirate flag which some men now wave in its place may be torn down and furled forever! Shall I condone the action of some, simply because they happen to be of my own race, when in Bushman or Hottentot I would condemn it? Shall men belonging to one of the mightiest races of earth creep softly on their bellies to attack an unwarned neighbor, when even the Kaffir has again and again given notice of war, saying, "Be ready; on such and such a day I come to fight you"? Is England's power so broken and our race so enfeebled that we dare no longer to proclaim war, but must creep silently upon our bellies in the dark to stab, like a subject people to whom no other course is open? These men are English; but not English-*men.* When the men of our race fight, they go to war with the blazoned flag and the loud trumpet before them. It is because I am an Englishman that these things crush me. Better that ten thousand of us should lie dead and defeated on one battle-field, fighting for some great cause, and my own sons among them, than that those twelve poor boys should have fallen at Doornkop, fighting to fill up the pockets of those already o'er heavy with gold.'

"And she said: '*You,* what does it matter what you feel or think? *You* will never be able to do anything!'

"And he said: 'Oh, my wife, stand by me; do not crush me. For me in this matter there is no path but one on which light shines.'

"And she said: 'you are very unkind; you don't care what the people say about us!' and she wept bitterly, and went out of the room. But as soon as the door was shut, she dried her tears, and she said to herself: 'Now he will never, never dare to preach such a sermon again. He dares never oppose me when once I have set down my foot!'

"And the man spoke to no one, and went out alone into the veld. All the afternoon he walked up and down among the sand and low bushes; and I walked there beside him.

"And when the evening came, he went back to his chapel. Many were absent, but the elders sat in their places, and his wife also was there. And the light shone on the empty benches. And when the time came he opened the old book of the Jews, and he turned the leaves and read: 'If thou forbear to deliver them that are drawn unto death, and those that are ready to be slain; if thou sayest, Behold, we knew it not; doth not he that pondereth the heart consider it? and he that keepeth thy soul, doth he not know it?'

"And he said: 'This morning we considered the evils this land is suffering under at the hands of men whose aim is the attainment of wealth and power. To-night we shall look at our own share in the matter. I think we shall realize that with us, and not with the men we have lifted up on high, lies the condemnation.' Then his wife rose and went out, and others followed her,—and the little man's voice rolled among the empty benches; but he spoke on.

"And when the service was over he went out. No elder came

to the porch to greet him; but as he stood there, one—he saw not whom—slipped a leaflet into his hand. He held it up, and read in the lamplight what was written on it in pencil. He crushed it up in his hand, as a man crushes that which has run a poisonous sting into him; then he dropped it on the earth as a man drops that he would forget. A fine drizzly rain was falling, and he walked up the street with his arms folded behind him, and his head bent. The people walked up the other side; and it seemed to him he was alone. But I walked behind him."

"And then?" asked Peter, seeing that the stranger was silent; "what happened to him after that?"

"That was only last Sunday," said the stranger.

There was silence again for some seconds.

Then Peter said, "Well, anyhow, at least he didn't die!'

The stranger crossed his hands upon his knees. "Peter Simon Halket," he said, "it is easier for a man to die than to stand alone. He who can stand alone can also, when the need be, die."   54–69

There is no man living who can conceive of its [Company's] age . . . Even here on this earth it began, when these hills were young and these lichens had hardly shown their stains upon the rocks, and man still raised himself upwards with difficulty because the sinews in his thighs were weak. In those days, which men reck not of now, man, when he hungered, fed on the flesh of his fellow-man and found it sweet. Yet even in those days it came to pass that there was one whose head was higher than her fellows and her thought keener, and, as she picked the flesh from a human skull, she pondered. And so it came to pass the next night, when men were gathered around the fire ready to eat, that she stole away, and when they went to the tree where the victim was bound, they found him gone. And they cried one to another: "She, only she, has done this, who had always said, 'I like not the taste of man-flesh: men are too like me; I cannot eat them.' She is mad," they cried; "let us kill her!" So, in those dim, misty times that men reck not of now, that they hardly believe in, that woman died. But into the heads of certain men and women a new thought had taken root; they said: "We also will not eat of her. There is something evil in the taste of human flesh." And ever after, when the fleshpots were filled with man-flesh, these stood aside, and half the tribe ate human flesh and half not; then, as the years passed, none ate.

Even in those days, which men reck not of now, when men fell easily upon their hands and knees, they were of us on the earth. And, if you would learn a secret, even before man trod here, in the days when the dicynodont bent yearningly over her young, and the river-horse which you find now nowhere on the earth's surface, save buried in stone, called with love to his mate; and the birds whose footprints are on the rocks flew in the sunshine, calling joyfully to one another;—even in those days when man was not, the fore-dawn of this kingdom had broken on the earth. And still, as the sun rises and sets and the planets journey round, we grow and grow. . . .

All earth is ours. And the day shall come when the stars, looking down on this little world, shall see no spot where the soil is moist and dark with the blood of man shed by his fellow-man: the sun shall rise in the east and set in the west, and shed his light across this little globe; and nowhere shall he see man crushed by his fellows. "And they shall beat their swords into ploughshares, and their spears into pruning-hooks: nation shall not lift up sword against nation, neither shall they learn war any more." "And instead of the thorn shall come up the fir-tree, and instead of the brier shall come up the myrtle-tree:" and man shall nowhere crush man on all the holy earth. To-morrow's sun shall rise, said the stranger, and it shall flood these dark koppjes with light, and the rocks shall glint in it. Not more certain is that rising than the coming of that day. And I say to you that even here, in the land where now we stand, where to-day the cries of the wounded and the curses of revenge ring in the air, even here, in this land where man creeps on his belly to wound his fellow in the dark, and where an acre of gold is worth a thousand souls, and a reef of shining dirt is worth half a people, and the vultures are heavy with man's flesh—even here that day shall come. I tell you . . . that here on the spot where now we stand shall be raised a temple. Man shall not gather in it to worship that which divides; but they shall stand in it shoulder to shoulder, white man with black, and the stranger with the inhabitant of the land; and the place shall be holy; for men shall say, "Are we not brethren and the sons of one father?"

. . . . Certain men slept upon a plain, and the night was chill and dark. And, as they slept, at that hour when night is darkest, one stirred. Far off to the eastward, through his half-closed eyelids, he saw, as it were, one faint line, thin as a hair's width, that edged the hill tops. And he whispered in the darkness to his fellows, "The dawn is coming!" But they, with fast-closed eyelids murmured, "He lies; there is no dawn."

Nevertheless, day broke.   70–74

Take a message to the men and women of this land. Go, from the Zambesi to the sea, and cry to its white men and women, and say: "I saw a wide field, and in it were two fair beasts. Wide was the field about them, and rich was the earth with sweet-scented herbs, and so abundant was the pasturage that hardly might they consume all that grew about them; and the two were like, one to another, for they were the sons of one mother. And, as I looked, I saw, far off, to the northward, a speck within the sky, so small it was, and so high it was, that the eye scarce might mark it. Then it came nearer, and hovered over the spot where the two beasts fed,—and its neck was bare, and its beak was hooked, and its talons were long, and its wings strong. And it hovered over the field where the two beasts were; and I saw it settle down upon a great white stone; and it waited. And I saw more specks to the northward, and more and more came onward to join him who sat upon the stone. And some hovered over the beasts, and some sharpened their beaks on the stones; and some walked in and out between the beasts' legs. And I saw that they were waiting for something.

"Then he who first came flew from one of the beasts to the other, and sat upon their necks, and put his beak within their ears. And he flew from one to the other and flapped his wings in their faces till the beasts were blinded, and each believed it was his fellow who attacked him. And they fell to, and fought; they gored one another's sides till the field was red with blood and the ground shook beneath them. The birds sat by and watched; and when the blood flowed they walked round and round. And when the strength of the two beasts was exhausted they fell to earth. Then the birds settled down upon them, and feasted, till their maws were full, and their long bare necks were wet; and they stood with their beaks deep in the entrails of the two dead beasts, and looked out with their keen bright eyes from above them. And he who was king of all plucked out the eyes, and fed on the hearts of the dead beasts. And when his maw was full, so that he could eat no more, he sat on his stone hard by and flapped his great wings."   80–82

There was a streamlet once; it burst forth from beneath the snow on a mountain's crown; and the snow made a cove over it. It ran on pure, and blue, and clear as the sky above it, and the banks of snow made its cradle. Then it came to a spot where the snow ended; and two ways lay before it by which it might journey: one, on the mountain ridges, past rocks and stones, and down long sunlit slopes to the sea; and the other down a chasm. And the stream hesitated; it twirled and purled, and went this way and went that. It *might* have been that it would have forced its way past rocks and ridges, and along mountain slopes, and made a path for itself where no path had been; the banks would have grown green, and the mountain daisy would have grown beside it; and all night the stars would have looked at their faces in it; and down the long sunny slopes the sun would have played on it by day; and the wood-dove would have built her nest in the trees beside it; and singing, singing, always singing, it would have made its way at last to the great sea, whose far-off call all waters hear.

But it hesitated. It might have been that, had but some hand been there to move but one stone from its path, it would have forced its way past rocks and ridges, and found its way to the great sea—it might have been! But no hand was there. The streamlet gathered itself together, and (it might be that it was even in its haste to rush onwards to the sea!)—it made one leap into the abyss.

The rocks closed over it. Nine hundred fathoms deep, in a still, dark pool it lay; the green lichen hung from the rocks. No sunlight came there, and the stars could not look down at night. The pool lay still and silent. Then, because it was alive, and could not rest, it gathered its strength together; through fallen earth and broken debris it oozed its way silently on; and it crept out in a deep valley; the mountains closed it around. And the streamlet laughed to itself, "Ha, ha! I shall make a great lake here; a sea!" And it oozed, and it oozed, and it filled half the plain. But no lake came,—only a great marsh,—because there was no way outwards, and the water rotted. The grass died out along its edges; and the trees dropped their leaves and rotted in the water; and the wood-dove, who had built her nest there, flew up to the mountains, because her young ones died. And the toads sat on the stones, and dropped their spittle in the water; and the reeds were yellow that grew along the edge. And at night, a heavy white fog gathered over the water, so that the stars could not see through it; and by day a fine white mist hung over it, and the sunbeams could not play on it. And no man knew that once the marsh had leaped forth clear and blue from under a hood of snow on the mountain's top; aye, and that the turning of one stone might have caused that it had run on and on, and mingled its song with the sea's song forever.   85–88

"In that small spot where alone on earth your will rules, bring there into being the kingdom to-day. Love your enemies; do good to them that hate you. Walk ever forward, looking not to the right hand or the left. Heed not what men shall say of you. Succour the oppressed; deliver the captive. If thine enemy hunger, feed him; if he is athirst, give him drink." A curious warmth and gladness stole over Peter Halket as he knelt; it was as when a little child his mother folded him to her: he saw nothing more about him but a soft bright light. Yet in it he heard a voice cry, "Because thou hast loved mercy—and hated oppression!—"   93

Stories, Dreams and Allegories

From "The Buddhist Priest's Wife"

J do not like to talk of any man who has loved me. . . . However small and poor his nature may be, he has given me his best. There is nothing ridiculous in love. I think a woman should feel that all the love men have given her which she has not been able to return is a kind of crown set up above her which she is always trying to grow tall enough to wear. I can't bear to think that all the love that has been given me has been wasted on something unworthy of it. . . . If a man tells you he loves you, . . . with his breast uncovered before you for you to strike him if you will, the least you can do is to put out your hand and cover it up from other people's eyes. If I were a deer . . . and a stag got hurt following me, even though I could not have him for a companion, I would stand still and scrape the sand with my foot over the place where his blood had fallen; the rest of the herd should never know he had been hurt there following me. I would cover the blood up, if I were a deer. . . .

. . . Yet, you know, I have not the ordinary feeling about love. I think the one who is loved confers the benefit on the one who loves, it's been so great and beautiful that it should be loved. I think the man should be grateful to the woman or the woman to the man whom they have been able to love, whether they have been loved back or whether circumstances have divided them or not. 72–73

God's Gifts to Men

The angels stood before God's throne to take down his gifts to men.

One said, "What shall I take to the little child?"

God said, "A long cloudless day in which there shall be no rain, to play in."

And one said, "What shall I take to the woman?"

And God said, "The touch of a little child upon her breast."

And one said, "For the man?"

God said, "He has all things, let him enjoy."

"And what shall I take for the poet?"

And there was silence for a little while.

And God said, "For the poet, a long sleep in which there shall be no dream, and to which there shall be no waking: his eyes are heavy."

And the angels went down.   124

They Heard . . .

The Poet and the Thinker sought for truth.

God bent and held a hand to either.

To the Poet he put out his hand from a cloudless vault of blue; the Poet saw it, and climbed.

To the Thinker God stretched his hand from the heart of a mighty cloud; the man looked up and saw it move: he mounted.

On far-off mountain sides they labored, looking upwards.

Then he who looked into the blue, cried: "Brother, you are wrong! What lies above you is but dark cloud; reach it—you will find it cold mist. In it you will wander forever. Over me in the blue sky is that which calls me; I rise to it!"

The Thinker answered: "Fellow, you are dazed. The sun has shone too long upon your head. What lies above you is an empty vault of blue. Enter it, you will find it empty space; you will grasp —air! Over me in that dark storm cloud lives that which calls me: when the lightning flashes and the thunder rolls and the cloud is riven, I see illuminated that which beckons. I mount to it."

The Poet cried—"Fool!"

The Thinker—"Blind!"

They both mounted.

At last, when they were very tired, they reached their mountain summits.

God bent, and took his Poet in his left hand, and his Thinker in his right, and laid them in his breast. When they awoke, they were side by side upon the heart of God. One whispered, "By the left hand, I!"; the other, "By the right!" . . . and they heard the truth beat.   125–126

The River of Life

A Soul stood on the bank of the River of Life, and it had to cross it.

And first it found a reed, and it tried to cross with it. But the reed ran into its hand at the top in fine splinters and bent when it leaned on it. Then the soul found a staff and it tried to cross with it: and the sharp end ran into the ground, and the soul tried to draw it, but it could not; and it stood in the water by its staff.

Then it got out and found a broad thick log, and it said, "With this I will cross." And it went down into the water. But the log was too buoyant, it floated, and almost drew the soul from its feet.

And the soul stood on the bank and cried: "Oh, River of Life!

How am I to cross; I have tried all rods and they have failed me!"

And the River answered, "Cross me alone."

And the soul went down into the water, and it crossed.   130

The Two Paths

A Soul met an angel and asked of him: "By which path shall I reach heaven quickest—the path of knowledge or the path of love?" The angel looked at him wonderingly and said: "Are not both paths one?"   133

Workers

In a far-off world, God sent two Spirits to work. The work he set them to do was to tunnel through a mountain. And they stood side by side and looked at it. And they began to work. They found that the place they had to work in was too narrow; their wings got interlocked. They saw they would never get through the mountain if they worked at it only from that one place.

And one spirit said to the other, "You stay here; I will go and work from the other side."

And it flew away. And they worked on, each from his side of the mountain. And after years in the dark, each one heard the sound of the other's axe, picking, and they knew they were getting near—that the other was at work.

But before they got to the center, these spirits' sleep-time came; and God sent other spirits to take their work and place.

But they had heard each other's axes picking, in the dark; that was enough for them.   136

A Dream of Prayer

I stood on the footstool of God's throne, I, a saved soul, and I saw the prayers that rose up to heaven go up before him.

And they floated up ever in new shapes and forms. And one prayed for the life of her son, and the sufferer prayed for rest, and the wronged for redress, and the poor for food, and the rich for happiness, and the lonely for love, and the loved for faith. And amid them all I saw a prayer go up that was only this: "Give me power to forgive," and it passed like a cloud of fire.

And years passed and I stood on the footstool of God's throne again and saw the prayers go up, and all were changed: he who prayed for love prayed now for power, he who prayed for ease prayed now for strength, she who had prayed for her son prayed now for his child; but I noted one prayer that went up unchanged: "Give me power to forgive."

Again years passed and I stood on the footstool of God's throne once more, and saw the prayers go up. Then among them all I noted one I knew; it said only: *"Give me power to forgive."*

And years passed and I stood there again. And the prayers ascended, and were all changed. And I heard a prayer, faint and low, which said: "Teach me to forgive." And I said, "Surely this may be granted now," for the voice grew weak.

And God said: "It is answered; even now I have sent Death with the message." 134–135

The Winged Butterfly

The insects lived among the flowers. They were all soft, lovely little creatures without wings.

By and by one little caterpillar began to have tiny lumps upon his shoulders that grew out and out. "Ah," said the others, "he is ugly, see, he is deformed." And the little caterpillar hid behind the leaves, and the lumps grew more and more, and at last they came out lovely little wings. Then he came back to his fellows, and they all said, "Oh, lovely little brother! Oh, lovely brother." And he shook his little wings, and he said, "It was for this I went away, for this to grow I was deformed." And he flew round. And he came to one that he loved and he said, "Come, climb with me and let us go and sit on that flower." And his comrade said, "I cannot climb; it tires me; I have no wings like you. Go alone." And he said, "No, I will go with you." And the other said, "I am going here in this little hole in the earth." And the butterfly tried to fold his wings and creep in after him, but he could not; . . . and he said to another, "Come, let us be companions." And the other said, "Yes, I like your wings, but you must walk by me; you must not use your wings and fly." And he said, "Yes, I will only wrap them down." And they walked a little way together. Then the other said, "You are going too fast; your wings blow you on; do go slower." And the butterfly held his little wings as still as he could. And the other said, "They stick up so; couldn't you lay them against your side?" And he said, "Yes." But when he held them against his side they ached so they nearly fell off. . . . And the other said: "What are you so slow for? I thought one with wings would go faster than another. I thought you were so beautiful when you were up in the air. You are very ugly now. What are wings for? They only draggle in the mud."

Then the little butterfly spread his wings and flew away, away, away; and he kept far from the others and flew about by himself among the flowers.

And then the others said, "See how happy he is flying about there among the flowers, he's so proud of his wings."

And one day the little butterfly sat on a rose, and died there.

And the others thought it died of drinking too much honey. None of them knew that it died of a broken heart.   151–153

The Adventures of Master Towser

I—HIS SORROW

Small Towser sat with his tail in a puddle of mud. The puddle was small, but so was his tail. His nose was turned down to the paving-stone; there were two drops running down towards the tip of it, but they weren't raindrops, though the afternoon was sad and cloudy enough—they came from his eyes. Presently, out of the swell gate of the house over the way came a most respectable-looking dog, of a very comfortable appearance, and as big as eight Towsers, for he was a mastiff.

"Why don't you take your tail out of the puddle?" asked the comfortable-looking dog.

Towser gave it a feeble little splutter in the mud; he didn't know why he let it hang there, except that he was miserable.

"Starve you over at your house?" inquired the comfortable dog.

"No," said Towser, "there are dishes of bones and nice little bits of fat in the kitchen."

"Other dogs bite you?"

"No." Towser shook his head.

"Have to sleep out in the cold?"

"No, I've got a house," said Towser.

"You're a nice gentlemanly-looking little dog; you oughtn't to be unhappy. What's the matter?" asked the comfortable-looking dog.

"I'm not any good," said Towser.

The big dog didn't comprehend.

"I want someone to love me," said Towser; "I want to help somebody; I want to be of use."

"Love!" said the big dog. "Did you ever smell it?"

"No," said Towser.

"Or see anybody eat it?"

"No."

"Or sleep on it?"

"No."

"Then what use is it?" said the big dog; and he went away.

Shortly after that Towser got up off the stone, and took his little tail out of the mud. He shook his little ears and let the two drops run off his nose.

"I'll go and seek for someone that needs me," said Towser; and so he started on his travels.

II—His Search

"I must look as pleasant as I can," said Towser, as he went down the street; and he perked up his little ears. He really was a pretty terrier, with long silky hair. Presently he saw a boy walking on the pavement. He was ragged, he looked as if he hadn't had any dinner or breakfast either. Towser's heart ached for him. He looked very lonely.

"I'm sure he would like a nice little dog like me to be a companion to him," said Towser. "Yes, he wants me; I won't trouble him for food, because everyone gives me something when I go to the back doors, because of my big eyes."

So Towser began dancing a little dance of affection, shaking his ears and looking from under them with his round eyes. This proceeding was meant to say, "I want to love you."

"Doggy, Doggy, Doggy!" said the little solitary boy, standing still and holding out his fingers; "Doggy, Doggy, Doggy."

So Towser came close up, just curling into a ball with excitement. He didn't know whether he should lick the little boy's hand first or his feet.

"There!" said the little boy. He gave Towser a powerful kick on the tip of his black nose.

When he looked back, Towser was standing quite still, with a great singing in his ears. Then the little lonely boy laughed.When the singing had left off, Towser trotted away down the street. He wasn't so ready to caper now. He saw several little lonely boys as he passed, but he didn't think they wanted him.

At last he got to the outskirts of the town. There was a bonny little house with roses and creepers all round. He went to the back door and put his fore-feet on the step, and looked in to see if there was anybody wanted him. A lady lay on a sofa in one corner; she had not walked for ten years, and her eyes were heavy with pain.

"Dear little creature, where do you come from?" she said.

Towser made a motion with his fore-feet, to explain that he would come in if he were invited.

The lady said, "Come in," and he sat down on the rug before her and the lady felt his ears.

"Beautiful ears," she said, "come!"

Towser jumped up on the sofa beside her.

"I never saw such large eyes," said the lady. "Dear little dog, if I can I shall keep you for my own," and she made a place for him on her chest.

He lay with his paws close to her chin, and looked as loving as he could. Presently he licked her chin, and she said he had a soft little tongue. When her lunch came she fed him with brandy and egg out of a spoon. He didn't like it, it burnt his throat, but he drank it.

"She wants me awfully, I can just see that," said Towser, "and I'll stay with her as long as I live."

The lady had him taken to her bedroom that night, and a nice little rug laid for him across the foot of her bed. In the night, when she woke to cough, he walked up to her face and licked it, and she covered him with the blankets till there was just the tip of his black nose sticking out.

"The big, comfortable dog said love was nothing, but it's something," said Towser, "and it's nice"; and he put his little muzzle against her cheek. Next day he danced before her, and tried to catch his tail when she looked sad.

"Oh, I'm a dear, nice, happy little dog; she does love me so. She couldn't live without me; I'm such a comfort to her," said Towser. He wished he'd been six months younger, then he'd have six months more to live.

So weeks passed.

One afternoon a lady came in.

"I've brought Nola home," she said, "so much better for her change to the sea-side; here she is." And the lady put down on the floor the most snow-white terrier (Towser was brown), all soft with curls, and with little sleepy eyes.

"She looks better," said the lady—"dear Nola."

Nola climbed quietly up on the sofa and curled herself up in a little nest and shut her eyes.

Towser stood looking on. He thought he would jump on the sofa, too.

"Down, Towser, down!" said the lady.

Then Towser went and got behind the crimson curtain, with only his nose and two bright eyes peeping out. At last tea-time came, and there was a dish of milk put down on the floor. Nola got off the sofa and went to drink some; Towser came out, and put his little black muzzle in too. As soon as the curly white one saw it, she lifted her pink nose, and got quietly back on the sofa.

"Nola won't drink with Towser," said the lady; "take him to the kitchen and give him a nice basin of milk with plenty of cream in it."

Then Nola got off the sofa again; but Towser wouldn't go to the kitchen. He got behind the curtain and looked out with his great saucers of eyes.

"It'll be bed-time soon, and I am sure she is wanting me badly to lick her chin. I'm sure she is wishing it was bed-time," said Towser.

"Make a comfortable bed for Towser in the kitchen, and be sure it's nice and soft," said the lady.

Towser wouldn't get into the bed; he sat on the stone looking at the fire. He wondered if a coal had got into his heart. He felt so wicked.

"I wonder what is the matter with Towser," said the lady the next day; "he used to be such a nice little dog, always so lively."

Then Towser got up, and began dancing about after his tail, and then he got on the sofa, and began playing with the lady's fingers and rings. Then the white curly one opened her eyes slowly and got off the sofa.

"Nola, Nola, come here! Down, Towser, down!" said the lady.

Then Towser went out in the garden and sat in the gravelled path looking up at the sun. I don't know how he felt.

"Towser's such a nice little dog," said the lady one day; "quite the nicest little dog I've ever seen. I wish I could get someone to take him away; someone who would be kind to him."

Now Towser didn't wait to be given away to a very kind person. I fancy he had a pain at his heart. He put his tail close between his hind legs, and went out at the back door.

III—His Reward

Towser sat alone in a wood. He leaned his head on a stone at his side. He was thinking; you could see that by his big, round eyes.

"I made somebody happy; that's a great comfort," said he (for all that there were tears running down his nose). "I must be happy; I must think I once made somebody happy"—here his little chest swelled out immensely. "It doesn't matter if you're not loved if only you've made somebody happy. Yes, I won't want to be loved any more, I'll just try to help people, and then I'll be happy too. You mustn't want to be loved; just to be good."

So he took his head off the stone and went trotting away through the wood. Presently he saw a country boy before him carrying a flitch of bacon; not long after from the bushes at the pathside burst a gipsy-looking fellow.

After a minute, the rough fellow said to the boy, "Give me your bacon."

Said the boy, "No."

The man said, "I can make you; there is nobody near."

He took hold of the bacon; the boy began to struggle. He knelt upon the boy. Then every hair upon Towser's little body stood on end, and his tail was stiffened out. He forgot he was Towser, he forgot he wanted to be loved, he forgot everything, and flew at the trousers of the gipsy man. Then the gipsy man thought there was someone coming, ran away, and left the boy and the bacon.

Towser stood in the middle of the path barking furiously. He was in great excitement.

Slowly the country fellow got up; his face was purple with rage. He cut a little stick from the bush growing by; it wasn't thicker than his finger; Towser's backbone was not thicker either.

"So, you stand here barking at me, do you?" said the country fellow. "Why don't you go after your master? You want to bite me! do you? do you? do you?"

Towser thought his little backbone would be broken, and when the stick hit his little skull it was terribly sore. The country fellow held him fast with one hand; he was so small he wasn't much to hold, and beat him on his little fore-feet and in his eye; then he took up his bacon, and walked away.

Towser went into the brushwood close by, and sat down on his tail and lifted his nose to the sky. The one eye was shut up, but the other was wide open, and the water running out of it.

If he ever went home and became a comfortable, respectable dog, I don't know; the last I saw of him he was sitting there in that wood.   109–118

From Man to Man

$\mathcal{S}$lowly advancing knowledge has forced on us an entirely new view of the Universe. Step by step we have been brought almost to the standpoint from which many an old Greek looked out on life.

For us once again the Universe has become one, a whole, and it lives in all its parts. Step by step advancing knowledge has shown us the internetting lines of action and reaction which bind together all that we see and are conscious of.

Between the farthest star and the planet earth we live on, between the most distant planet and the ground we tread on, between man, plant, bird, beast, and clod of earth, everywhere the close interneted lines of interaction stretch; nowhere are we able to draw a sharp dividing line, nowhere find an isolated existence. The prism I hold in my hand, rightly understood, may throw light on the structure of the farthest sun; the fossil I dug out on the mountainside this morning, rightly studied, may throw light on the structure and meaning of the hand that unearths it; between the life that moved in the creature that plowed in the mud of the lake-shores three million years ago and the life which beats in my brain and moves in my eyes here in the sunshine today, I can see long unbroken lines of connection. Between spirit that beats within me and body through which it acts, between mind and matter, between man and beast, between beast and plant and plant and earth, between the life that has been and the life that is, I am able to see nowhere a sharp line of severance, but a great pulsating, always interacting whole. So that at last it

151

comes to be, that, when I hear my own heart beat, I actually hear in it nothing but one throb in that life which has been and is— in which we live and move and have our being and are continually sustained.

Having this view of the nature of the Universe forced on us, is it possible that our view of the nature and value of truth should not be changed?

The physiologist, when he seeks to study an organism, puts beneath his microscope an almost invisible spot of blood or shred of animal tissue, and devotes days or months to its study, not because he believes the individual shred or speck to be of any peculiar value, but because he knows that once rightly under- stood, it may explain to him the nature of the entire organism of which it is a part. So we, who are dominated by this new concep- tion of existence, are compelled to look upon the exact knowl- edge of even the smallest and most insignificant fact as sacred, never knowing when it may turn into the key which may unlock for us the meaning of part of that great universal life of which it is an integral fragment.

Holding this view of the Universe, we are compelled to walk almost awefilled among even the small things of life; and, as the old Christian father, after much contemplation, was compelled at last to cry, "There *is* no small sin—all violation of the will of God is great," so we also are almost compelled to cry, "There is no small truth—all truth is great!"

Holding the old conception of existence, it was quite possible to believe that, between God and man, mind and matter, soul and body, there were many chinks and crannies where a lie might creep in and hide itself and be quite innoxious. For us there is no faith in such possibility; we can no more nurse a false concep- tion without it causing injury than a foreign substance can be intruded into a highly organized body without causing disorgani- zation and disease. Whether the truth concerns the feathers on a pigeon's wing or the constitution of a lump of earth or a psychological fact, we know that it is vital.   154–156

The new mother, when she looks down at the little head upon her breast, whispers in her heart: "Oh, may you seek after truth. If anything I teach you be false, may you throw it from you, and pass on to higher and deeper knowledge than I ever had. If you are an artist, may no love of wealth or fame or admiration and no fear of blame or misunderstanding make you ever paint, with pen or brush, an ideal or a picture of external life otherwise than as you see it; if you become a politician, may no success for your party or yourself or the seeming good of even your nation ever lead you to tamper with reality and play a diplomatic part. In all the difficulties which will arise in life, fling yourself down on the truth and cling to that as a drowning man in a stormy sea flings himself onto a plank and clings to it, knowing that, whether he sink or swim with it, it is the best he has. If you become a man of thought and learning, oh, never with your left hand be afraid to pull down what your right hand has painfully built up through the years of thought and study, if you see it at last not to be founded on that which is; die poor, unloved, unknown, a failure—but shut your eyes to nothing that seems to them the reality."   158

The great criminal was not necessarily the murderer, the ruffian, the drunkard, the prostitute, or even the frank, direct and open liar; but, maybe, a spirit encased in a fair and gentle body, rich in many graces of character and manner, openly breaking no social law and with no need to lie directly to others, because it lies always and so successfully to itself and within itself and acts so persistently in harmony with that lie; a rotten apple with dead seeds and a worm at its core, and a shining surface. The old view was that the great sin lay in not speaking truth to your fellow when thereby you caused him practical loss; for us there is one infinitely greater—the sin of the soul that refuses to see the naked truth within itself and therefore can never show it. The man who lies to his fellow poisons an external relation—but the soul which lies in itself to itself, acting always a part before itself, becomes a poison, a deadly fungus that scatters its poisonous seeds unconsciously whenever it is touched.   159–160

The story, the picture, the statue in which certain artistically necessary aspects of life are intentionally suppressed or misrepresented for certain practical ends, the human nature falsely painted because it seemed undesirable to paint it as it is, the fig-leaf tied across the loin of the noblest statue, gives no pain and is still art; while, for those of us who have long set an intellectual value on sincerity, a mental habit has been formed which makes the perception of the willful suppression of truth emotionally painful and so destroys our sense of perfection in the object in which it appears. The true reproduction of a sunrise, or a narrative that shows the working of a lofty spirit, may be more delightful art for us than the art which reproduces the texture of a lady's dress or paints the picture of a small soul; but the representation of the smallest or slightest aspect of life, if we are conscious of truth in it, insofar satisfies an emotional need in us and becomes for us, so far at least, an object of satisfaction; while no art can be art for us, however lofty its claims, which does not satisfy what has slowly become a master need of our natures. A work of art may have many other elements of beauty for us; but it must be a revelation of truth for us, or it means nothing. Better the true picture of a beggar in his rags than the willfully false picture of a saint.   160

Why, when a nation or race or a dominant class has reached a certain point of culture and material advance, has it always seemed to fall back from it, and the nation or race or class to be swept away? Always the march of human progress has died out there, to be taken up again by some other race or class in some distant part of the globe or after the lapse of centuries—to die out there also after a time, never proceeding persistently in a straight line. Was there an immutable law, based on an organic and inherent quality in human nature, which caused this arrest? Was it futile for us to hope that human advance might ever proceed persistently and unbroken in one direction? Was that which governed its arrest an organic law, like that which ordains the length of a man's beard, which, however long the individual may live, when it has once reached a certain length will always stop growing? Is it absolutely futile to hope that humanity can ever advance as the fern palm grows, beautiful frond beyond beautiful frond opening one out of the other as it mounts up higher and higher?—or has the arrest and decay, so invariable in the past, being merely dependent on external and fortuitous conditions, having no one organic root in the human nature itself and therefore being possible to avoid?   162–163

That all so-called advanced societies have, in the past, always disintegrated and fallen back does not prove that a hard rim-line exists which humanity can never surpass, and cannot prove this while we are in possession of a fact which adequately accounts for this retrogression without any such supposition.   163–164

What was that high point of advance, intellectual and moral, which we speak of Greece having attained in the fourth century before Christ, and from which she receded so quickly and completely—was it indeed Greece which ever reached that point? What was that much vaunted culture, that high creative energy, that passionate thirst after intellectual insight, that demand for personal freedom, that search after physical beauty, but the possession of a few males who constituted the dominant class in a few cities of Greece! What was that much-vaunted culture but a delicate iridescent film overlying the seething mass of servile agricultural and domestic slaves and of women, nominally of the dominant class, but hardly less servile and perhaps ignorant, who constituted the bulk of its inhabitants? As little could it be said to have been the property of the inhabitants of the land of Greece as the phosphorescent light on the surface of the ocean is the property of the fathoms of water stretching below it whose surface it illuminates. It would be as rational to expect that such a form of culture, brought into existence for a moment by a combination of happy conditions, could hand itself down from generation to generation, expanding and strengthening as it grew, as to expect a spray of shrub, plucked and placed in a vase of water in a hot-house, though it might bloom profusely for a few days, should permanently propagate itself and persistently grow when it was without ground and had no root.

But even had things been otherwise in Greece—had its women, they who alone have the power of transmitting the culture and outlook of one generation safely to the next, been sharers in the culture and freedom and labors of its males, not merely partially in the person of a few of its *hetairai,* but in that of the bulk of its child-bearing women—had every hand that labored in the fields or the cities been that of a freeman, sharing to the full the civic rights of his State, possessing a stake in its material welfare and a culture that enabled him to rejoice in its art and share in its thought—had that happened which never yet has happened in any land—had Greece been filled with a population homogeneous in their culture and freedom—had no untaught servile woman existed to suckle any Greek child—had no slave formed a rotten foundation stone in the social structure—had culture, freedom, and civic rights been the common property of every human who breathed on the soil of Greece—had the social superstructure been sound and homogeneous from foundation to coping stone;—even then, though the vantage gained, instead of passing away in a couple of generations, might have remained for a few hundred years and there might have been more persistent progress; yet,—could it have been even tolerably permanent?

For what was the whole of Greece itself but a mere spot on the earth's surface? What were its people but a drop in the ocean of humanity? Unless she could have walled herself in, shutting off all possibility of interaction with all the races beyond herself, sooner or later she must have been so interacted upon by the mass of humanity beyond, that change and disintegration, moral and intellectual, must have set in, and she must slowly have fallen back to the common level.   164–165

All the civilizations of the past, in Egypt, in Assyria, in Persia, in India, what had they been but the blossoming of a minute, abnormally situated, abnormally nourished class, unsupported by any vital connection with the classes beneath them or the nations around? What had they resembled but the long, thin, tender, feathery, green shoots which our small rose trees sometimes send out in spring, rising far into the air, but which we know long before the summer is over will have broken and fallen; not because they have grown to a height which no rose tree can ever attain, for ultimately the whole rose tree may be much higher than the shoot, but because they have shot out too far before their fellow branches to make permanence possible; having no support, wind and weather will sooner or later do their work and snap them off or wither them. Next year a dozen rich young shoots may sprout from the snapped stem and survive; it may not have shot upwards and been broken off without helping in the growth of the whole tree—but it, itself, perishes.

If the whole of our vaunted modern advance, our science, our art, our social ideals, our material refinement, were to pass away tomorrow, swept away by the barbarians we nurse within the hearts of our societies or which exist beyond: would it for a moment prove that humanity had reached its possible limit of growth, and not rather that a sectional growth is no permanent growth?—that, where the mass remain behind, the few are ultimately drawn back? . . . Would it prove that our loftiest ideals of human progress were futile?—man moving ever in a little ring, advancing and forever falling backward as soon as the edge is reached—and not merely that the true cry of permanent human advance must always be "Bring up your rears! Bring up your rears"? Head and heart can ultimately move no farther than the feet can carry them. Permanent human advance must be united advance!   165–166

If the advance of a nation or a race must always ultimately be stayed, partly because of the internal action of the undeveloped mass within itself which must in time disintegrate it, and partly because the interaction with humanity beyond itself must ultimately draw it down and back, how much more must it be the case that a solitary individual city can never reach its full development in a society far behind itself?   167

That the highest and most harmonious development of the individual which we dream of is never reached, and that the attempt to attain it seems always to lead to intense personal suffering or absolute social destruction for the individual striving, in no way proves that the ideal is ultimately beyond reach—an *ignis fatuus* which the human hand will never grasp. As the nation or the class which should first have developed so far that it turned all its energies entirely away from the creation and wielding of the arts of destruction and self-defense, and turned them entirely to the creation of the beautiful and useful arts which benefit all mankind, would, ultimately and probably very soon, be swept away, as long as anywhere on the earth's surface there were still races so retrograde that they devoted all their energies to the arts of destruction; and as the nation, which should have attained the moral standpoint at which it became no longer possible for the stronger to absorb all the good of life and in which therefore poverty and need become extinct, would inevitably be overcome by the wanting and miserable products in other societies where a lower moral standard prevailed, if any such society existed anywhere on the earth—so more surely the individual, who should arrive at a higher moral point of development and strive to realize his ideals in actual life, must inevitably suffer or be absolutely annihilated in a society which had not reached his standpoint; and this not because his ideal was inherently unattainable and might not be the ultimate goal of his race, but simply because, for its realization harmoniously and successfully, it wanted more than the solitary unit, it wanted the interaction of the whole society.

A wolf who should suddenly be smitten by the idea that, instead of tearing his fellows to pieces, it would be better if they made a league of cooperation and fellowship, and for that purpose filed down his canines, would quickly become a prey to his fellows, not because his ideal was incompatible with successful animal life, for other forms have attained to it, but because its attainment by one was impossible.

So the individual primitive man in a cannibal tribe who had become possessed with the idea that the eating of human flesh was undesirable, and who had refused to capture and feed, would have become an object of scorn and probably of hatred to his tribe, and might probably have died of hunger in some time of pressure, not because his ideal was ultimately unattainable, for today practically the whole of humanity has reached it, but because change in the idea of his fellows and the common carrying out of agricultural and pastoral labors were necessary to its successful attainment.

The man who dreams today that the seeking of material good for himself alone is an evil, who persistently shares all he has with his fellows, is not necessarily a fool dreaming of that which never has been or will be; he is simply dreaming of that which will be perfectly attainable when the dream dominates his fellows and all give and share. Working it alone, it fails, because the individual is part of an organism which cannot reach its full unfolding quite alone.   167–168

The man whose ideal it is that, by the non-requital of injuries and the large expansion of sympathy even towards those who inflict suffering on himself, is human good and justice finally served— does his failure to evoke any response, and his final crushing beneath the hands he refused to strike, prove anything but the solidarity of humanity and that the foremost branch which grows too far beyond its fellows must ultimately be snapped off? That no individual ever yet realized in life the highest development which the mind has dreamed of does not prove that perfect truth and fellowship are not attainable to humanity, but that the one alone cannot compass them.

Is it not a paradox covering a mighty truth that not one slave toils under the lash on an Indian plantation but the freedom of every other man on earth is limited by it? That not one laugh of lust rings but each man's sexual life is less fair for it? That the full all-rounded human life is impossible to any individual while one man lives who does not share it? "Bring up your rears! Bring up your rears!"   169–170

You say, and rightly, physical health and strength are among the prime necessities of the fully developed human creature. The Kaffir and the South Sea Islander have often these in their very highest perfection; are these, therefore, the races to be preserved and which others are to be sacrificed for? You say a powerful reason is essential to the advance of the race; you find your man with the powerful reason, but diseased, antisocial, using his powerful intellect only as a means of preying on his fellow, often the great criminal. You say, at least let us kill out the hopelessly unfit, the invalid and the sickly and the consumptive; under this law you may ordain to destruction the bright, the lovely and most beneficent of the race. Has my view not as much to be said for it as yours that, if any on earth should be willfully destroyed as the down-drawers of the race, it is not a Shelley or a Keats, who has enriched and beautified existence on earth beyond fifty thousand whole men; but that it is the man of perfect physical health, with far less intelligence, and organically incapable of living for anything but his own well-being, finding no joy in any kind of sacrifice for his fellows and transmitting his qualities as surely as the consumptive or the weak, who is really the disease point in humanity, the creature who prevents the noblest social institutions and personal relations from coming into existence, because his egoisms can always be calculated to make them unworkable? You say that keen perceptions and the power of dominating are characteristics of the to-be-preserved races, but what if to me the little Bushman woman, who cannot count up to five and who, sitting alone and hidden on a koppie, sees danger approaching and stands up, raising a wild cry to warn her fellows in the plain below that the enemy are coming, though she knows she will fall dead, struck by poisonous arrows, shows a quality higher and of more importance to the race than those of any Bismarck? What if I see in that little untaught savage the root out of which ultimately the noblest blossom of the human tree shall draw its strength? Who shall contend I am not right?

You say, "Let it be granted that social qualities are to count as high or higher than intellectual or physical, then at least it will be justified that all avowedly criminal individuals and classes should be destroyed."—But who are the criminals? You say the prostitute, the murderer, the robber, the gambler. But who are these? The judge who sits in his elbow-chair sentencing the man who plays pitch and toss in the street and himself sits up 'til two o'clock over his cards—the king and the prince who, while every avenue of pleasure and good is open to them, hang around the tables of Monte Carlo. . . .   171–173

. . .For on that broad road of opposition to law and authority, along which stream the millions of humanity too low to grasp even the value of laws and institutions about them, resisting them from an ignorant and blind selfishness which makes them believe they are improving their own conditions by violating them, there are found walking men of a totally different order—white-robed sons of the gods with the light on their foreheads, who have left the narrow paths walled in by laws and conventions, not because they were too weak to walk in them, or because the goals towards which they led were too high, but because infinitely higher goals and straighter paths were calling to them—the new pathfinders of the race! These men, who rise as high above the laws and conventions of their social world as the mass who violate them fall below, are yet inextricably blended with them in the stream of souls who walk in the path of resistance to law. From the Monk Telemachus, who, springing into the Roman arena to stop the gladiatorial conflict, fell, violating the laws and conventions of his society—a criminal, but almost a god—up and down all the ages man has been on earth there have been found these social resistors and violators of the accepted order, the saviors and leaders of men on the path to higher forms of life.

It is true that if, persistently and with a rigour from which none escaped alive, you could in every land exterminate the resistors of social law, you might at last produce a race on earth in which even the wish or the power to resist social institutions will have died out; your prisons might be empty, your hangmen and judges without occupation. But what would you have done? Seeking to cut out humanity's corns, to remove its cataract, to amputate its diseased limbs, you would have put out its eyes, cut off its tongue, maimed its legs; unable to see or move or express, its heart would beat slower and slower and death would come.

There is no net which can be shaped to capture the self-seeking ignorant violator of law which shall not also capture in its meshes the hero, the prophet, the thinker, the leader—the life of the world!

As the oak tree cannot grow unless, with each new ring it adds, its old bark cracks and splits, so humanity cannot develop without the rupture of its old institutions and laws; and it has been exactly because the bulk of humanity have never of necessity been able to distinguish between this healthful disruptive process and unhealthful decay, and have sought to crush and annihilate the particles causing it, that the growth of humanity has been as slow as it has. To suggest the more rigorous extermination of all non-law-submitting humans is simply to suggest a slow suicide as far as human development is concerned. In all ages, the multitude has looked upon Barabbas as a less violent and dangerous disrupter of social laws than the Christ—not this man, but Barabbas! . . .

But, you may say, granting that we cannot determine who the criminals are who should be destroyed for the benefit of the race, or the kind or degree of ill health which should be followed by instant destruction, yet surely such an ideal body of humans should find no difficulty in desiring the annihilation of all dark and primitive races who are manifestly a down-draught on humanity.

But, are they so?

Is there really any superiority at all implied in degrees of pigmentation, and are the European races, except in their egoistic distortion of imagination, more desirable or highly developed than the Asiatic? Are we not in our vanity like the parvenu, who, having wrung wealth out of the labor of others and surrounded himself by the results of all human toil and knowledge, stands in his gorgeous room filled with the works of art and use of all nations, and, with his hands in his pockets and his full belly, looks around with infinite satisfaction at what he has accumulated about him, and says, "All these are mine," believing really that their existence and creation has something to do with himself? Are we modern Europeans not the parvenus among the human race? From the ancient civilizations of Asia and Africa, ancient and complete, when we were merely savage, have we not got all the foundation and much of the superstructure of what we possess? Art, science, letters, all are their original creation, merely taken over by us; even our very religion, such as it is, we could not invent for ourselves, but had to take it over from a hook-nosed, swarthy, Semitic people. And, if the learning and art and industry of Asia and Africa, passing into the hands of that marvelous bloom of humanity, the Greek race, in its little span improved and enlarged what it took, it yet has been no work of ours, the northern barbarians; we were running naked and staining ourselves with woad in our woods when the looms of India and China were producing the delicate fabrics we seek now to imitate, when Asiatics ate from golden-flowered and delicate china, when temples and statues were raised that are our wonder and admiration, when philosophers taught and thought, and books were written and great legal systems enacted, while we sat round our fires on the dung and gambled with knuckle bones or danced war dances to the shouts of our fellows. It ill becomes us, who are but the tamed children of yesterday, to talk of primitive savages. Even today, when we have inherited all, is it so certain that our vaunted civilization is so much statelier and on all sides wider and with nobler elements of truth lying at its foundation than the older civilizations of the yellow and brown races? Is it so sure we are

the people and wisdom will die with us? Is it not possible, for
instance, that there is something of deep wisdom in the Chinese
ideal which gives so much of the beauty of life to the end, which
gives even the woman when she is old, the mother and grandmother, so honored and tender a place in society? Is it quite wise
to sacrifice all to youth, so that every man and woman fears old
age and would sacrifice all to avoid it? Must not the whole of life
be more beautiful when men wait for good at the end, the joy of
the sunset? Is not the religion which permeates Asia, and which
came to life while our fathers still dreamed of heaven as a hall
where man drank wine from the skulls of their enemies, more in
harmony with the teaching of modern knowledge, which is re-
shaping us, than even that other Asiatic religion which we have
adopted? Did not the deep-seeing eye of the Buddha, hundreds
of years before the Jewish teacher walked in Syria, perceive
clearly beneath all the complexities of form and individuality the
unity in life upon the earth? He did not get at it as the modern
man of reason, slowly, by measurement and calculation; by deep
perception he knew that our little brothers look out at us from
the eyes of animals, that the life of no beast and bird or insect is
alien and unconnected with ours, that life flows on earth as one
large stream with many divided branches, and under his mystical
doctrine of the transmigration of souls he covered the same radi-
cal truth which "evolution" expresses in other but perhaps more
absolutely accurate terms. We northern fair-skins have had great
men; our glimpses of new truths, new masteries over matter, have
added our grain to humanity's sum of riches even in the direction
of creative art; but, when we look around us on what we call our
civilization, how little is really ours alone and not drawn from the
great stream of human labors and creation so largely non-
European? We scorn the Chinaman because his women compress
their feet, not perceiving how infinitely more deadly and gro-
tesque is the compression of our bodies; we ridicule, in certain

Asiatic races, the pigtail of the Chinaman or the darkened tooth
of the Japanese, blinded by egoism to the infinite degradation of
the northern races in their passionate strife to imitate ever-
changing costumes and modes, alike so far removed from nature
and beauty that even we, when a few years are past, perceive their
grotesqueness and vulgarity, the slavish imitation of fashions
which, by their unending change, feed on the vitals of the race
through their ignoble demand on the brain of its womanhood,
absorbing energy, reason, imagination, and setting, so long as
their diseased reign lasts, a limit to the progress and expansion
of woman, and, with her, of the race. We accuse of immorality the
Asiatics who consume the opium we forced upon them at the
point of the sword; but we fair northerners deserve today, as fully
as when the Roman spoke it two thousand years ago, the judgment that, as a people, our chief pleasures were drinking and
gambling; our race courses and card tables are as essential to our
happiness as the dice and knuckle bones to our forebears. Is it
not more than possible that, infinite as has been the debit of
humanity to the ancient non-European peoples in the past, they
have yet more to confer in the future?   174–179

Is it not possible that man, a creature of the plains and hills,
naked and always in unbroken activity in the free air, cannot
survive beyond a certain time when he goes about loaded with
materials from all the vegetable and animal and mineral king-
doms which he has gathered from all the quarters of the globe
—as a mantis collects mud and shells to make a case for himself,
when he buries himself deep among his little erections of mud
and stone, shutting off from body and brain light and air, when
he has so constructed life that half of his body social is parasitic
and enervated by want of labor, and the half it feeds with crushed
under the superimposed weight—is it not possible that the primitive man, individually and structurally as well as socially, may, in

some future aeon, have the same restorative function to fulfill towards ourselves as we imagine ourselves to have played toward older decadent civilizations? . . . Were not our forebears so to Greeks and Romans? Were not Attila and the Huns so horrible, physically and mentally, in their eyes that they were believed to be the offspring of witches and evil spirits, nothing wholly human being possibly so repulsive? Was it not death to the Roman woman who wedded a barbarian? To have eaten or drunk or slept with him was disgrace. He was supposed even to have an unendurable smell. Was the difference not at least as great between the lovely cultured Greek and the trained imperial Roman, between Pericles and Virgil, and the naked and spear-brandishing long-haired savage, drinking blood from the skulls of his enemies, as between his modern descendant and any primitive savage on earth? Who shall say that, in destroying the child of nature with his perhaps simpler organization, and untried nerves, we are not destroying that of which humanity may yet in the aeons to come have need to keep the race upon the earth?

At the worst, which is fairer and more akin to the ideals towards which humanity seems to move?—the little Bushman in his open cave on the mountain brow, etching away into the rock with his little sharpened flint the picture of hunting or wild beast, and looking down in the glory of sunshine on the place below where the wild things graze, or a swell-chinned ragged woman staggering out of a public-house in one of our centers of civilization, while the man who made the drink dwells in high places? Which is lovelier here, now, or in any place or time—the troop of men and women on a South Sea island, naked and gladly disporting themselves in the water or wandering together in the sunshine and sharing their love in the open light of day, or the scene that night by night our great cities witness? Which fills us with a sense of the greatness of the human spirit—the Kaffirs on their flat-topped mountain refusing to surrender month after month, 'til the conquerors, when they mount at last, find only one or two hardly-moving skeletons—men, women and children having died with hunger—or the civilized soldier who has sworn to die, but when a tenth part of his numbers have fallen, puts up the white flag, willing to take life but not to lose it?

He needs be a brave man who would dare ordain destruction to all primitive and barbarous people, who could feel so sure humanity will have no need of them on her march through the future.

But letting all those difficulties pass . . ., supposing it were possible for us to find an individual, a class or a race, so constituted that it presented in itself all the conceivable disadvantages and deficiencies which can afflict human nature and none of the advantages; supposing it were possible—which it never would be—to find anywhere a body of humans as diseased, as devoid of physical health and the vital enjoyment of life as a worn-out man of fashion and debauch, as stupid and ill-shaped as a Bushman, as brutal as the savage, as false as the worst civilized man, as antisocial as the criminal, as hypocritical as the Pharisee, physically deformed and mentally wanting, combining in itself all the drawbacks of each form and stage of human growth and none of the advantages—you may say: "Here at least we have found at last the creature or class whom, to perfect its own growth, it is necessary society should slay and mercilessly destroy." But is this so? If such individual or race were found, would it even then be proved that the highest use which society could make of them would be to destroy them? Does not the essential element, which it is most important to develop, if human life on earth is ever to attain to its full blossoming, lie in just that very sensitiveness towards the right of existence of all other human units, that deep-seated and at last organic desire not to benefit ourselves at the cost of others, which this course of action would tend to blunt and kill? In attempting to remove the undesirable and, to us, retrograde portions of human society, are we not blunting and striking at the very existence of the quality in ourselves which is above all essential to full human unfolding? Might not an immensely more productive use be made of such undesirable elements of life, by using them as objects for the development of those broad and generous human feelings which are the crowning beauty of life? In seeking to exterminate the undesirable of the race when we find him, may not society be striking at the very heart of its own progress, inflicting a mortal wound upon itself which exceeds in deadliness any which the undesirable individuals could have inflicted on it? Is it not an act of moral suicide?

And . . . if even this point also were waived, if it be allowed that it might be possible to find a body of humans so perfect and impartial that they are fit to legislate for the race, and that it might be possible for them to discover persons and races so hopelessly undesirable that for the benefit of the race's growth they must be destroyed; yet there remains the second great difficulty—who would bell the cat? Supposing this body of enlightened impartial and thoughtful humans decided that tyrants, drunkards, gamblers, murderers, robbers, hypocrites and all inflicters of suffering on their kind, and stupid and blindly narrow persons were an evil to the race and should be destroyed—would this enlightened and philosophic body of persons be themselves able to carry out their edict of destruction and become captors and executioners? And, if they had to delegate it to others, would not the very persons to be destroyed be often the persons fit and able to carry it out? The debauched judge, the ignorant, stupid and narrow jailer, the brutal and stupid soldier, the bloodthirsty tyrant, the very individuals ordained to destruction, may be the most impossible to get at. You may condemn Nero, but you cannot compel him to destroy himself, and you may not be able to find anyone capable and willing to do so. The very conditions of lofty intelligence and wide unbiased sympathy, which would alone endow any human being with the gift necessary for impartially judging for the race, are the very qualities which might render him unfit and incapable as executioner.

But, you may say that this is merely irrelevant child's play; that no sane person supposes you could find a body of humans wise enough and impartial enough to determine for the whole race which are the retrograde elements which must be destroyed for its benefit or powerful enough to destroy them when it has so determined; that the same end is attained much more securely and quickly by simply allowing all the physically stronger elements in humanity everywhere to destroy the weaker; that by the stronger everywhere destroying the physically weaker with a wonderful automatic action, all that is undesirable in humanity is killed out and all that is desirable remains. But is this so? . . .

You say this is the great law of the survival of the fittest which leads to all beauty, strength and unfolding in sentient life; that to interfere with it in any way is to interfere with nature's one plan for attaining perfection.

You shelter yourself under the name of science. Are you not, and one-eyedly, perverting the teaching of great minds, as the priestly in all ages pervert and make falsehood of the perception of the great prophets who preceded them? . . .

You say all evolution in life has been caused simply by this destruction of the weaker by the stronger.

From every cave and den and nest, from the depths of the sea, from air and earth, from the recesses of the human breast, rises but one great "No!" that refutes you. Neither man nor bird nor beast, nor even insect, is what it is and has survived here today, simply because the stronger has preyed on the weaker. The law of its life and its growth and survival has been far otherwise. From the time when, in a dimly living form, amoeba sought and touched amoeba, and, meeting, broke out into a larger form and divided into fresh forms, life has been governed, step by step, through the long march and advance in stages of life, by union; love and expansion of the ego to others has governed life. From the insect, following that unself-conscious reason we call instinct, who climbs to the top of the highest bough to fasten there her eggs where the tender shoots will first sprout to feed on them, on to the bird who draws the soft down from her breast to warm the nest, who toils to feed and warm, and hovers about before the feet of the dangerous stranger that he may be drawn to attack her and not find her young, and who draws up the food from her own crop to feed them, 'til love becomes incarnate in the female mammal feeding her young from her breast—this is my blood which I give for the life of the world—through all nature, life and growth and evolution are possible only because of mother-love. Touch this, lay one cold finger on it and still it in the heart of the female, and, in fifty years, life in all its higher forms on the planet world would be extinct; man, bird and beast would have vanished and the cold dim dawn of sentient existence would alone exist on a silent, empty earth. Everywhere mother-love and the tender nurturing of the weak underlies life, and the higher the creature, the larger the part it plays. Man individually and as a race is possible on earth only because, not for weeks or months but for years, love and the guardianship of the strong over the weak has existed. You may almost estimate the height of development in the creature by the amount of mother-love and care he stands for.

You may say that mother-love forms an exception in the rule of nature, which, for perfecting life, demands the destruction of the weak by the strong. But, what of the protective care of the male, not only of his own young and his related females, but of all the most helpless of his group? It is not only the sea lion who carries about his young in the bag on his own person; but through all sea life runs the defense of the weak by the stronger. Could the ostrich breed out its eggs in the wastes, where long journeys for food are needed, if the male did not daily take his hours of brooding on the nest to keep the eggs warm and care for and watch over the young with a tenderness even greater than their mother's while she goes afar to seek for food? Could the female bird of many kinds rear and feed her young without the continual aid of the male? Nor is it only parental sympathy, but a much wider feeling for the weak, which makes possible much of the higher animal life about us. It is not only for the defense of his own young that the old stag stands ceaselessly watching for danger and raises his shrill cry when he sees it approaching, at the greatest risk to himself. I have seen upon a cliff a baboon stand defending the one defile where dogs could mount, hurling them down with his hands and glancing back every moment anxiously to see how the troop of males and females carrying their young were escaping, clinging to his post 'til he fell, torn to fragments by the dogs, saving his race and his species, not by his vast power of destruction, but by his willingness to be destroyed that others might live. The survival of the mierkat, so small and defenseless on the barren plains where so many other creatures become extinct in the presence of danger and of enemies, is accountable only when you know that each mierkat acts for all; not for their own young only, but for each other, and, for the younger and more helpless, all labor and sacrifice themselves. When the hawk approaches, if the older males and females be gone out far to look for food, tiny creatures, themselves hardly weaned, will seize all the tinier ones half an inch shorter than themselves and in desperate anguish strive to carry them off to the hole, forgetting all fear for themselves in their passionate attempt to save those who may have no blood relationship with themselves, while the older males and females grow gaunt and thin in the breeding-time, because almost all food they find is brought to lay at the feet of the young, while mothers go away to seek food which will supply the quite small with food. Is this passionate love for one another, this endless self-sacrifice of all, this devotion to the weaker by the stronger, which makes it possible for these little, delicate furry creatures with their beautiful eyes and small powers of defense to survive in our terrible, barren, enemy-filled plains. The panther and the lion have vanished in the terrible presence of man, and many other forms of life grow very scarce, but these tiny creatures are still surviving, aided by their passionate devotion and self-sacrifice.

Then among men in their very struggles with each other, is it always the strongest fist and the fiercest heart which aids races or individuals to survive? Has not a great love lain behind those marvelous victories of which the world's history is full, where small and relatively weak nations and individuals have survived and driven back the large and powerful—a love for an idea, for a race, for a land, which, by blotting out personal considerations, has given weakness the power to protect itself and survive? The legend of the Swiss who gathered a score of spears into his breast, and so made room for his fellows to break the phalanx and win their nation's freedom, is only emblematic of one of the deepest-seated transforming and preserving forces in human nature. The legend of the mother, which in varying form almost every country possesses, who, to save her child from the bird of prey, climbed where the foot of the bravest and strongest could never tread, to recover it, is universal, because it outlines the profound truth recognized everywhere that an almighty affection and the instinct for even self-immolation in the serving of others is not merely one of the highest but one of the strongest forces modifying human life. Almost everywhere in the record of human life on earth are the traces of rapine and slaughter and the suppression or destruction of the weak form by the strong; and they have left their marks not only in the heavy and, to us, hideously protruding jaw and beetling eyebrows of the male gorilla, dividing him from the more human female and young, but giving him that strength of bony structure which is necessary to enable him to rend and destroy; not only in the structure of the scorpion, all sting and tail, so loathsome from the human standpoint, that, were it not that it bears its young upon its back, it would seem so unredeemably repulsive as to be none other than a nightmare; but it may have given the springbuck her long, graceful legs to flee from the jaws of her enemies, and have brightened the eye of the gazelle to see in the far distance the destroyer and to aid in its escape. It may even have rendered more intense some of the most complex emotions in the higher animal, because the species in which individuals were most inclined to defend the weak at their own cost may have survived where more purely self-centered varieties fell. It has played its part, and a vast part, in the history of life on earth. But to regard this destructive element in existence as the key-note to life on earth is a strange inversion. When we look from a hilltop on a herd of wild antelope on the plain below us and two old males come into conflict and desperately wound and perhaps kill one the other, the very fact that we are so struck by the incident and absorbed in watching shows it is not the universal, the all-pervading element, of the life before us. The care of the young by the mother, the drawing of sex to sex, the feeding together in good-fellowship of hundreds of creatures—all this rouses no curious remark in us, because it is but of the universal substance of life that things should be so.   180–188

From the mysterious drawing together of amoeba to amoeba, their union and increase, on through all the forms of sentient life, and in the life of the very vegetable world, the moving, original power is always this stretching-out, uniting, creative force; shaping itself in the union of male and female, of begetting with their begotten; drawing together creatures of like and unlike kinds, bringing into all the forms of friendship and union and love, it lies at the root of existence; it shapes the petals of flowers, not for death but to call the insects to suck their sweetness and carry fertilizings to one another; it sings in the song of all song-birds calling to their mates; it blossoms into human speech; . . . to kill, man might have been silent; but to communicate with and bind himself to his fellow, child to mother, the sexes to reach each other, man, to reach man belonging to his social organism, man was obliged to blossom into speech. Everywhere this binding, moving creative force moves at the very heart of things, growing more and more important and complex as the creatures mount in the scale of life, 'til it reaches its apotheosis in the artist, in whom the desire to create dominates all else, who, not from himself but by the necessity of some force within himself, is spent and must spend himself to produce that which gives infinite joy without ever being used up, over which there need be no strug- gle; for not-seeing the statue or not-hearing the story or not- singing the song makes others poorer. Men have so recognized that this creative (and not the destructive) power was the fount and core of life that in all ages they have tended to call the highest intelligence they could conceive of, and therefore their supreme God, "The Great Creator"; and their devils have been destroy- ers. It is false to say that the mighty jaw and the almighty claw and the stomach that is never filled and is always seeking to fill itself, are the fundamental moving power in life—

> 'Tis love that makes the world go round,
> The world go round, the world go round!   189–190

But you may say that, granting love and self-obliteration in the cause of others plays a dominant part in the sentient life among kindred and groups, and that the mysterious instinct to create and continue to reproduce lies as the fundamental hidden power manifested in all we call life—granting all this, yet you must allow that, at least between species and species and distinct groups, a terrible conflict has always gone on, that this victory of the strongest jaw and the longest claw and the biggest belly has resulted in the survival of the fittest, and that, in the world in which this strife has gone on, we have many beautiful things— singing birds, flowers, the wonderful intelligence of man and beast—this has grown up under the struggle!

Yes, the struggle has gone on and the fittest have survived. The fittest?—to survive; not of necessity the fittest in any other sense in which we humans use the word.

The fittest has survived! Under water, half-buried in mud, only the outline of the jaw and two deep-slit eyes show where the alligator lies. Age after age, he has lain in the mud and slime. The gazelle has come down to the water to drink and has been drawn in by the mighty jaw; the little monkey, delicate, quick, high-witted, swinging from branch to branch and stretching its hands out to dabble in the water, has come too near, and the brown stump has moved and snapped it up; the human child has come to play upon the bank and disappeared; the young girl has come to draw water and only her broken pitcher has been left on the mud to show where she was drawn under; all have gone to fill the almighty maw and been crushed by the mighty jaw; the creature survives. In the ages which have passed since it came into being, many fair and rare forms have existed and passed out of exis-tence. The little winged creatures with large eyes and brains, reptile in order but fitted for flitting in the air and sunshine, whose images we find impressed on the rocks, have gone; they may have had rare and beautiful colors for anything we know, and may have had notes of song, but they are gone; fishes and birds and beasts that have been, have passed forever; even in our own ages, lofty forms of life have passed and are passing away; but the alligator survives. Not because it was more fair, more beautiful, more complex, more brave, than the creatures upon whom it lived or whose stay on earth it outstayed, but because its long jaw set with serrated teeth, its dead, solid hide, its absorption simply in seeking food for itself, its torpid, half-buried existence on mud banks and amid slime, fitted it to destroy the complex, pulsating animals and to outlive the beautiful aerial forms which had not its almighty jaw and its mighty stomach. It was fittest to survive. The boa constrictor wakes in the morning and before night, bird and beast have been crushed in its mighty folds; it lies stupified and torpid with the creatures it has consumed in its expansive inside. It has survived them, not because it was fairer or higher in the scale of being than they, but because so greasily and silently it could creep on them. The cobra strikes dead man and beast, and survives, not because she is braver or higher or even stronger, but because beneath that tooth she carries that little poison bag and strikes so silently and it may be in the dark.

If a ship full of poets and philosophers and men of science, bound for some distant place of meeting, were wrecked on the shore of Africa, and a cannibal tribe met them, they would be consumed. The savage would rub down and oil his sides with the fat of the poet; the brain of the philosopher would frizzle before the fire; the cannibal's belly would be full of man of science and artist; in a time of famine, the cannibal might survive and beget his kind, when a neighboring tribe died out from hunger for want of timely poet and thinker! Would the fact that he had eaten poet and philosopher prove that he was higher than the men who filled his belly and gave strength to his muscles? The fittest to survive —but the fittest for what else? Even when nation sweeps out nation, what does it mean? Is it always the loftier, more desirable form that survives? When the barbarian swept Greece 'til Athens was left like an empty and bleaching skull, is it certain that the savage was higher than the race which he supplanted? In nearly two thousand years in that land of blue seas and mountains, he and his descendants have produced nothing that the world prizes or desires. The fittest survived!—the fittest for what?   190–192

Singing birds are with us, insects of beauty and color, beasts of intelligence and heroic forms, and man, who, in spite of all, has instincts and powers latent within him of rare beauty, and strength, reason, imagination, sympathy and joy. Yes, this we have—but, oh, for the songs that will never be heard on earth now!—for the beauty we shall never see!—for the forms of light and glory which will never flit among earth's trees!—for the creatures of intelligence and complexity that will never tread earth's floor!—Oh, the might have been. . . . what has been saved, we know; what has been lost, we shall never know. The gorilla and chimpanzee are with us; but what if, in some hidden forest, a yet more beneficent, intelligent type arose, developing quite away from the predatory to a more social form, 'til, meeting with the stronger-armed, heavier-jawed gorilla, it was exterminated, and one line of beneficent growth shut off forever? It is difficult to understand how what we call man ever came into being—the manikin thing with such small physical powers of defense and attack, whose young, for years, in spite of mother-love and male protection, could so easily fall a prey to any wild beast, and who, at its best, is physically small and powerless—unless he first, for long periods, developed in small, sheltered situations where attacks from predatory saurians or more modern carnivora were rare; but what if somewhere, it might be among inaccessible mountain peaks and valleys in the dim times when man was shaping, a branch existed in whom, in time, having to expend no great force in purely predative or physically self-defensing directions, the germ of other faculties developed higher artistic and musical and reasoning powers, deeper and broader powers of originality, all that for the last many millenniums we have been slowly and with difficulty marching towards when the conditions of life have allowed; if this variety ever were thrown into contact with a more gorilla-like form intent on destruction, it must have been swept away; that one act of destruction, would have delayed

the march of humanity for ages—nay, prevented it forever perhaps from attaining certain noble and, to us, desirable shapes.

If it were possible for us to land upon a planet in most things
like our own and launched on its course with ours, it is quite
possible we should find upon it a being as much higher, and from
our standpoint, more desirable, than our highest ideals are
higher than ourselves; our early stage of sentient growth might
have been the same, and this difference, now so vast, might have
arisen merely because, once or twice in the course of growth
through the aeons, their highest intellectual and moral type
might have escaped destruction by its lower. . . . is it not still
within us in such mighty force, because age after age, not merely
those races but those individuals in whom its existence was weak-
est have been killed off by the individuals most incarnate of the
lower nature and not allowed to perpetuate themselves freely,
either physically or spiritually? Lies are so easy to us because age
after age, the lying and subtle and insincere have conquered and
crushed the individuals in whom sincerity and openness were
budding. It is so difficult for us to consider others justly and
impartially if they have terribly injured us, because age after age,
the individuals striking most mercilessly at whatever limited their
pleasure, without consideration of justice or sympathy, have
killed out and suppressed those in whom generosity and justice
were beginning to dawn. Lust, divided from all love and inborn
self-forgetfulness, is so dominant within thousands of us (making
the world of sexual relations, which in our ideals are the highest,
often the lowest, in life), because age after age, the most brutally
lustful has perpetuated himself, where the less lustful and brutal
has failed to rape and force the woman or kill the opposing males.
Because, age after age, the individual tendency to expend force
in the direction of impersonal intellectual activity has again and
again fallen victim to the individual more concentrated on personal aim, we today find the complex intellectual gift of the

thinker and artistic creator so rare and so heavily conflicted with by the lower opponents. Because the stronger sex has so perpetually attempted to crush the physically smaller, the individuals who attempted to resist force by force being at once wiped out, sex has acquired almost as a secondary sexual characteristic a subtleness and power of finesse to which it now flies almost as instinctively as a crab to the water when it sees danger approaching, the struggles against which being the sternest that sex has to carry off within itself if it would attain moral emancipation. Because the larger male has so long and so mercilessly suppressed the weaker, and exterminated those who refused to submit while the servile survived, we find perhaps, that lowest of all human qualities, the material tendency to truckle before success and power, which in some humans seems instinctive and in them at least is ineradicable. For it is not alone through the physical destruction and annihilation of the weaker by the brutally stronger that we have suffered. What has humanity not lost by the suppression and subjection of the weaker sex by the muscularly stronger sex, alone? We have a Shakespeare; but what of the possible Shakespeares we might have had, who passed their life from youth upward brewing currant wine and making pastries for fat country squires to eat, with no glimpse of the freedom of life and action, necessary even to poach on deer in the green forests, stifled out without one line written, simply because, being of the weaker sex, life gave no room for action and grasp on life? Here and there, where queens have been born as rulers, the vast powers for governance and the keen insight the sex possesses have been shown; but what of the millions of the race in all ages whose vast powers of intellect and insight and creation have been lost to us because they were physically the weaker sex, whose line of life was rigidly apportioned to them at the will of the stronger, which governed the structure of their societies? What statesmen, what rulers and leaders, what creative intelligences have been lost to humanity, because there has been no free trade in the powers and gifts of the muscularly smaller and weaker sex?

Therefore, let no man lay the flattering unction to his soul that, by rushing out and destroying what is weaker than himself, or that, by using and bending to his own purposes all that live in the society in which he lives, he is thereby aiding nature in the great and lofty and perfect life on earth. The struggle between sentient creatures and the conquest by the most cunning, the most merciless, the most consuming, the muscularly or osseously stronger, has had powerful effects on the shapes which life takes on; it may have added to the keenness of the eagle's eye, the length of the springbuck's graceful bound; it may even have added to that intensity of anguished love which makes one baby mierkat try to drag a smaller away to safety when it sees the hawk approaching, because the little people have learned by a long racial experience what the claw and beak mean, and those who have loved and aided each other most have survived—the fittest to live, not the fittest to kill in that case!—it may have sharpened the wits of all creatures who had to escape, as the poison bag of the serpent teaches great caution in the country where it prevails(we always part the grass with our foot as we walk—though it might be just as well to walk without parting!); it has left many beautiful and curious forms of life, but has also destroyed many; it has nursed into being all the vices which lie deep buried in sentient life; it has age after age, killed out among advancing human creatures, the individuals, who, to reason, love, or any of the impersonal ends of life, sacrificed the arts of destruction and self-defense; it has hanged its Christ and poisoned its Socrates; it has nurtured in every one of us the brute which we shrink from in another when he turns it to us; it has killed out the winged reptile and a thousand noble, complex and brilliant forms of life, and has saved the crocodile and the python. The only strength which it directly preserves is predatory strength, strength of reason, strength of self-government, strength of affection, all the forms of strength most prized by the human creature as it advances, are not preserved of any necessity by it. The struggle between the forms of sentient life and action within a species, and the survival of those most fit to destroy, have no more made existence what it is than the road on a mountainside makes a mountain. It has modified, in some directions powerfully modified, the external forms of life, but no more made it what it is than a hatchet used to chop trees in an orchard makes the trees; the hatchet, wisely used, or by accident so used, in lopping off certain branches may make the trees bear larger or more fruit; but used otherwise, it may entirely destroy the tree, and, used recklessly and by chance, might cut down the whole garden. The process of pruning itself, however wisely carried on to produce certain ends, is an entirely subsidiary process, whose end, in increasing the size of abundance of the fruit, may generally be equally attained by manuring and feeding the tree; but it fails utterly to account really for the tree, whose essential life and essence lie in its power of growth, in the mysterious power of absorbing and adding to its substance in certain directions and along certain lines and of reproducing itself. All the pruning and cutting off in the world can never account for the fundamental mystery of one bud becoming a flower, for one grain of matter in the soil or particle of gas in the air being transformed into bark, for the kernel and reality of life. Pruning is a process which creates and produces nothing new, but which, wisely used, may tend to accelerate vitality and desirable variation; which, applied haphazardly, may produce mixed desirable and undesirable results, and which, used unwisely, may mean absolute destruction. Therefore, let no man lay the flattering unction to his soul that, by destroying all he can destroy, and using and consuming all he can use or consume, he is aiding nature in the only way possible in perfecting the human race on earth. Let him not imagine when he prates of the survival of the fittest that he is enshrouding himself and his desires in impenetrable armor; he is only an ass masquerading in the scientific lion's skin put on hind-side before!

You say that, with your guns shooting so many shots a minute, you can destroy any race of men armed only with spears; but how does that prove your superiority, except as the superiority of the crocodile is proved when it eats a human baby, because it has long teeth and baby has none? You say the fact that you can command the labor of so many of your fellow men and gratify your desires proves that you are higher than they; it proves that your belly is large and your power of filling it great; but what, in these matters, are even you compared to the old saurians with their vast claws and paws and rough tongues, who could have licked you off the face of the earth in a moment? The theory that humanity can be perfected on earth only by the stronger jawed, longer clawed, biggest bellied preying on the smaller is a devil's doctrine bred in the head of a fool.   192–198

If the perfecting of humanity is not to be accomplished by this destruction of one part by the other, how, then, is it to be accomplished? . . .

Is it not possible only in two ways? Is there any hope of our in any way raising and hastening the rate of human advance if we cannot do it by the killing out and suppressing of individuals?

Surely there are ways. Has not the human only now, at last, command of two vast means for the modifying of life and conscious perfecting of humanity? In that strange and lovely power which enables us to see and picture that which we have not in all parts ever fully seen, in the ideals which are clear before the human spirit, have we not the goal to be moved towards? And in our powers of reason, the means to find, step by step, the paths that lead to them, have we not now reached a plane of life, in which the struggle for existence that is to perfect human life need not in any sense be one between individual lives but between qualities within the individual—a struggle within each man to be fought mainly here . . . , here, where alone, each man rules omnipotently and where alone the kingdom of heaven on earth he dreams of can be brought to pass—here, where the ideal must be formed and realized, or nowhere? Has not the time when the slow perfecting of humanity can find no aid from the destruction of the weak by the stronger, but by the continual bending down of the stronger to the weaker to share with them their ideals and aid them in the struggle with their qualities? Is it not by the passionate, persistent determination to realize within ourselves our highest ideal, and then, by that strange power which makes every man's life unconsciously a voice calling to his fellows to follow, to be able to call on those who have not yet seen so far? Is it not so, and not in any other way, that the real blossoming time of man on earth will ever come? And no man liveth to himself and no man dieth to himself. It is not by destroying and crushing.   198–199

When the Spirit of the Ages, whose moments are millenniums, whose minutes are aeons, and whose hours are a human eternity, passed amongst the worlds of space, seeing how it fared there, he chanced on a planet. A wide plain stretched there, no trace of plant or shrub was on it anywhere, and burning sands stretched everywhere; but, far away in the distance, rose mountains; on their sides, one could see that streams flowed and that the earth was green and trees waved. Alone in the center of the plain stood a woman's figure, bare and beautiful from the waist upwards, but clothed below in a coarse garment. Its eyes were fixed on the distant mountains; again and again as it looked, it wrung its hands and tears streamed from the beautiful eyes. And the Spirit paused in its flight and lit on the earth beside her, and it cried, "Beautiful one, why do you stand here weeping, alone in this desolate spot, where no fair thing is, and the snake has left his track in the sand at your feet and the only foot-print is the mark of the wild beast's claw? On the mountains there is verdure; surely birds are singing among the trees and the grass is heavy with flowers; why linger here in this desolate spot?" But she wrung her hands and cried, "I cannot move; always and always, I look out for one to come and deliver me and take me with him to the mountains, but he never comes." And he said, "Beautiful one, your forehead is high, your bosom is full, your arms are strong, your hands well knit; why cannot you move forward?" And she wept and raised the robe that was about her, and the Spirit saw that, while from the waist upwards she was fair and powerful, from the waist downward, she was ill-nourished and loathsome. About her feet were iron fetters, upon the limbs were marks of unhealed stripes, old gangrenous wounds festered there, and the flesh was shrunken from the bones and the feet deep-sunken in the sand. And she cried, "My head is clear, my heart is sound, my arms are strong, but my feet, my feet, they bind me here! . . . I bind them with chains in my anger. It is they, it is they who keep me here!" And again she wept. The Spirit dropped his wing and drew nearer to her and whispered, "Despairing one, no deliverer will ever come. You, you, yourself must save yourself. From those weak limbs, strike off the fetters; with your strong hands, bend down and heal the wounds your hands have made; remove the sand about the heavily sunken feet. When they are healed and free and strong, they, they and not another, will bear you to the mountains where you would be." And he asked her, "What is your name?" And she answered, "My name is Humanity." And he said, "When the years have flown, I shall return again and see how it fares with you." And he smote his wings together and rose upwards: and Humanity was alone upon the plain.   200–201

Conversation Between Mother and Sons

I have dreamed that as we are living here in this old world, just as we have always lived, suddenly there has arrived among us a strange, terrible, new race of people, coming from I know not where, perhaps from the nearest star.

I have dreamed they were like us in body and mind, but with terrible white faces; our skins are tinted, but theirs were white as the driven snow, and their hair like thick threads of solid gold.

They talked and laughed just as we. Mothers brought their little babies into the world and trained and cared for them, and men and women had friends and relations that they loved, and when they died as we die bitter tears were shed into the new graves. When they were struck their bodies felt pain, and when they were insulted they resented it; they lived, living and fearing and hating and hoping, and in the end their bodies turned to dust like ours. They were human; but there was this difference between them and us—that, of many things, they knew what we did not, and they could do things we could not.

We, here on earth, have been so proud of our little cities and our little inventions, our ships and our books and our telescopes and our laws and our manners, and we have thought we were so wise and knew right from wrong, but, suddenly, when these terrible white-faced strangers came among us, all changed. The cities we had taken ages to build they shoveled away in a few days, and in their places raised palaces so large that our cathedrals went into their cellars. They had learned how to grasp the force of the tidal wave and of the very movements of the earth, and to use it as they would. Where we with difficulty dug holes a few hundred yards into the earth, they with their wonderful machines cut in miles, as though it had been cheese. They had machines that drew great currents of cold air down from the higher regions to cool the tropical plains, and they could send vast currents of warm air up to heat the mountain peaks. They sent currents of warmed air and water to the poles to make perpetual spring there, and cooled the equator with water from the poles. If they wished to speak to one a thousand miles off, they spoke and were heard, how we could not tell; and when they wrote they did not use their hand, they set something against their brains and the thoughts registered themselves. To go to the other side of the earth they had no need to use our little trains and ships; they passed through the air, and the highest mountain peaks warmed by hot currents from the plains were their resting places. They had instruments so delicate you could see the blood beat in the leg of a gnat no bigger than a pin's point; and others so strong you could see a pebble no larger than a thimble lying on the moon's surface, just as we now with our telescopes see the extinct volcanoes. They laughed at our dirty habit of putting diseased matter into our veins to save us from disease and of pouring poisons into our stomachs to mend all parts of our bodies. They had found out what it means when you say a thing lives and grows; they knew what passed on in our bodies, and when anything went wrong they knew how to go back to the cause to put it right. They called us savages. In their laboratories they shaped the most rare and delicious foods from gases and primitive atoms —foods such as we can get only when they have been drawn from the earth and air and combined in the living laboratories of the plants and animals. In every mouthful of food they ate they knew just how much of each substance the body needs was in it, and what the effect would be; they did not eat in the dark whatever came, as we do. The bloody flesh of our fellow creatures which we feed on, the roots we dig out of the ground too, the milk drawn out of the bodies of other living beasts, they thought as horrible and unclean as we think the grubs and entrails on which the Bushmen feed. And our clothes—the skin of dead creatures which we fasten over our hands and feet, the jackals' and bears' and skunks' skins which we hang about our shoulders with the tails flying and think ourselves so grand in, the feathers of birds and the dead birds which we mix with grass straws and fasten on our heads, the shreds of hair and wool from animals' backs, the threads from the insides of little worms, the torn decayed fiber of plants that we beat into clothes and are so proud to carry about everywhere on our bodies and think others savages if they have not got them—they thought disgusting.

They were so civilized they knew the body of a human being was more wonderful and beautiful than any covering matter made out of dead animals or decayed plants, and when they wore any covering it was only for warmth or to fasten on their wings. What they wore were beautiful scale-like things, woven as we weave glass out of sand, but soft and of many colors, fitting each human being's body as perfectly as their own skins; so that, when a man or woman was fitted out for flight with their wings on, they looked as a dragon-fly looks when it is hovering over a pool. They thought our clothes and the way we hid our bodies from light and air uncleanly; and they turned their heads from us, as we turn our heads from natives dressed in skins and rubbed with fats.   397–399

There are civilized men all over the earth, and we are proud of belonging to them. We despise the men who have not the material things we have and who have not learned to read and write, who have not the command of the stored-up knowledge of the ages; we despise them as the half-civilized Kaffir and Hottentot despised the Bushman.

And yet—and yet—Englishman and Frenchman, Chinaman and Greek, Hindu and German, Zulu and Japanese, Roman and Hottentot—if we go far enough back we all have to come together and stand before that cave door. The lady in her white satin with her jewels and broidered handkerchief, the king with his crown, the judge in his ermine, the poet and the thinker, the millionaire and the beggar, the warrior and the slave—we all stand huddled there; and, as we peep over one another's shoulders and bend to look in, we have still to whisper to what we see there—"Father!—Mother!" . . .

Perhaps you will say, "Yes, we know we were savages once, but what we are so proud of is that we are not now. We are right to despise the people who do not possess the things we possess and have not the knowledge we have. We are right to despise them and to call them Inferior Peoples and to treat them as it would [? not] be right they should treat us."

But have we really any right to fill out our chests so proudly? Is it really our civilization—yours and mine—made by us?

. . . . Look at this little book! . . . "It is our book," you will say, "written and printed in English by Englishmen"; and perhaps you feel a little proud that even small English boys of ten and eleven can read it and understand all that is in it when the great chiefs and leaders of many barbarous nations could not. But how much of it have we made? Look at these little black lines and dots! . . . You will say they are only the alphabet, something so simple that even babes . . . can learn them. Yes, and any fool can learn a thing when once it has been invented and another teaches him how to use and understand it—but who made them?—not we!

. . . . From the old cave days men made pictures of birds and beasts and men on cave walls and stones and trees and bones; and at last a time came when they found these pictures could be made to speak to others. Sometimes I think I see a man carving figures with a flint on the stem of a tree; the sunlight about him is the sunlight of a day scores of thousands of years ago. He is drawing the pictures there, so that the friends whom he has lost in the chase may know he has been there, and he is the first man writing.

As the centuries passed some men went farther; they learned to give each picture a meaning: a raven meant death and a serpent meant life, and a circle meant time, for instance; and then they would write long sentences in pictures, saying what men feel and think as well as what they say. And then the time came when men found that, by turning the pictures into short signs, by leaving out many lines they could write quicker—and so men wrote thousands of years ago in Egypt and Assyria and China. Then a time came when somewhere men found out the greatest thing men had discovered since they found out how to make fire; some men found out that if you used the signs not to mean words but simply sounds and put them together you could express at once and easily everything the human brain could put into words and the human lips utter—then there was the alphabet as we know it. For thousands of years men in Asia and Africa and on the shores of the Mediterranean labored; the Phoenicians passed it on to Greece and Rome; and so to-day we read and write with it. Look at these little lines . . . You will say they are only figures that any simpleton can read and even calculate with.—Yes, but each one of them has a history thousands of years old, since that time when our little first fathers and mothers first began to count upon their fingers and were proud when at last they could reach five. Countless millions of men have counted and thought and invented that these little simple signs might exist; and, if the Arabian figures had never come to us from Asia, some of the work we are most proud of doing could never have been done. . . . Perhaps you think it very clever that little lads . . . can tell the names of all the planets and how far they are from the sun, and tell much about the movements of the stars; but thousands of years ago, on the great solitary plains in Asia, dark-faced men through long nights lay and watched the stars, and in solitary towers night after night they watched how the heavens shifted and what rose and what set, and how the seasons of the year were marked; and, but for the labor of these solitary watchers, whose names we shall never know and whose very nations have passed away, the telescopes and observatory and calculations of which we are so proud could never have come into existence; they laid the foundations down; we raise the walls! The very paper of which this book is made:— You will say, "At least that is ours made out of rags spun in English mills and beaten into paper in English factories." But, when I hold these paper leaves between my fingers, far off across the countless ages I hear the sound of women beating out the fibers of hemp and flax to shape the first garment, and, above the roar of the wheels and spinnies in the factory, I hear the whir of the world's first spinning wheel and the voice of the woman singing to herself as she sits beside it, and know that without the labor of those first women kneeling over the fibers and beating them swiftly out, and without the hum of those early spinning wheels, neither factory nor paper pulp would ever have come into existence. If I tear one sheet of paper out of this little book and there were some being wise enough to tell me its whole story, with all the lines and dots and marks upon it, and what they mean and how they came to be, and how the leaf itself came into being, the whole story of the human race on earth would have to be told me, from the time our little forefathers and mothers rubbed two sticks together and made light. This little book!—this little book! —it has got its roots down, down, deep in the life of man on earth; it grows from there. It is not your book, it is not my book, it is not the African's book, or the Asiatic's book, or the European's book; it is THE WORLD'S BOOK!   406–409

We must always remember that, only the other day, as we count days in the life of men on earth, not even so many centuries ago as a savage would count on the fingers of his two hands—so short a time ago that perhaps the lichens which are growing on the rocks that have fallen from Table Mountain were growing exactly as they are to-day—our forefathers, yours and mine, were savages wandering naked in their woods and on their steppes, staining their bodies with colored juices, wearing as their only covering the skins of wild beasts, and building for themselves huts of mud and straw.

There were civilized men on the earth then. The Hindu had already built his great palaces and written his great books; the Chinaman had long wrapped his body in soft silken robes, and in delicately furnished rooms was sipping his tea out of China cups so delicate we cannot even now imitate them. The Medes and the Persians and Egyptians and nations whose names we do not know had had their great empires and their civilizations and had passed away; but we all the while lived the life of naked savages.

Even the Greeks had gathered their learning from Asia and Africa and had already written their great books and carved their great statues and reared their great temples, while our forefathers were dancing naked round their wood fires at night. The Romans had built roads and cities and made collections of laws; they looked upon our savage Northern forefathers as *"something hardly human"; "more like beasts than men"* one old writer called them. And if a Roman woman had married one of your ancestors and mine, the time was when they would have buried her alive as one who had eternally disgraced her race and people. And if they captured one of our ancestors and took him to Rome to follow one of their triumphal cars, he stared about him in the streets with the same stupefied wonder at all he saw, as a Zulu from the heart of Zululand, if he had never left his kraal, would stare if you set him down in the streets of London or Paris. Perhaps they were wrong to despise us so; there are ways in which a Zulu chief may be higher than a learned professor—but we were savages!   410–411

And sometimes even when I am walking in my garden and I see the peach tree covered with blossoms in the corner and the roses and lilies growing all round, and the grapes hanging from the table, and all the small flowers sending out their scent, the feeling comes to me, and I want to say—"To all the gardeners that have been before me—to the little old first mother, who scratched earth and put in roots and grasses—to Chinaman and Persian and Egyptian and Babylonian and Indian, and men and women of races whose names I shall never know, without whom I should never have this beauty—Thanks!" And sometimes as I work there I feel as if they were working beside me and the garden belongs to them and me. And sometimes I think perhaps in years to come, when I have long ages been dust, some woman working in a garden more beautiful than any I can dream of now will stretch out her hand and say—"To all the gardeners that have been before me—" and I, so long dead in the dust, will live in her heart again. . . .

You know, up-country on the great plains, where the camel thorn trees grow, there are ant heaps as high almost as a man. Millions of ants have worked at them for years, and slowly and slowly they have grown a little and a little higher. Sometimes I have fancied, if a little ant should come on the top of one of these heaps, and should rear himself on his hind legs and wave his little antennae in the air, and should look around and say, "My ant heap, that I have made! My ant heap, from which I see so far!— My plains—my sky—my thorn trees—my earth!" and should wave his little antennae and cry, "I am at the [beginning] of all!" —and that then suddenly a gust of wind should come! The ant heap would still be there, the ant heap on the top of which he chanced to be born; there would still be the trees and the plain and the sky; but he would be gone for ever.

I have sometimes wondered: Isn't it a little bit so with us, when we walk about so proud on the top of our little heap of civilization? Because the most that any man can hope for, and the most that any nation can hope for, is this: The man, that, in the one little hour of life that is given him, he may be able to add one tiny grain, so small perhaps that no eye will ever see it, to the heap of things good and beautiful which men have slowly been gathering together through the ages;—the nation, that, when its time to pass comes as it comes to all, it may have added to the things good and beautiful, which humanity lays up through the ages for the use of all, one layer, perhaps one thin layer, but that so well and truly laid that all coming after shall say—"It was nobly done."   412–413

And so, when I hear people talking of superior races and inferior peoples, and of keeping other races and peoples down, I hardly understand. Because, if I find people who seem to know a little less or to see a little less than I do, I always feel I want to say to them, "Oh little earth-brother and sister, climbing with me that long climb out of the dark, through the cave doors and on we do not know up where,—if it should happen that I have climbed on to a step a little bit higher than the one you stand on and can see a little farther—here is my hand—let me help you up."

. . . . Out there in my garden there are flowers of all kinds growing—tall queen-lilies and roses and pinks and violets and little brown ranunculuses—and I love them all. But if the tall queen-lilies were to say, "We must reign here alone, all the others must die to give place to us," I do not know, but I think I might say, "Is it not perhaps then best *you* should go?"

And perhaps the next day there might come a blighting frost; the rose bushes would live on and the little violets hidden at their roots, and even the little brown ranunculuses sheltered by higher branches, would be alive; but the lilies—the tall white queen-lilies —would all be dead!

I am glad there are all kinds of men and animals living on the earth where I live, that I and men like me are not the only creatures. If the time should come when there was only one kind of creature left, then the blooming time of the gods' garden would be done, and I would be glad to creep away under the dust and sleep.   417–418

"You mustn't think I don't understand, laddie; . . . I am your mother and three times older than you, and I ought to be much wiser; but when I go down the Government Avenue, and the colored girls sitting there laugh because they see I don't wear stays as other women do, it's as if a knife ran into me under my ribs. I know I'm right; that in years to come people will wonder women could be so mad and foolish as to deform themselves. And yet, when these women laugh at me, I am so full of pain I can hardly walk down to the station; and when I come home I feel I want to creep on to the bed and cry. I've tried to like colored women and do all I can to help them, and then they jeer at me! I don't want for days to go out again. If I, your mother, who should be so much stronger and wiser, feel these things so, what right have I to expect that little boys like you can bear them? You would be heroes if you could. . . .

    "You know, laddies, . . . you are always talking of being *men*, and how fine it will be when you are grown up. It is a finer thing to be a 'man,' than either of you can know now. But it's not being able to lift a great weight or strike a great blow or crush things beneath you that can ever make you that. The thing that really matters is this: that, when that day comes, as it must come to you at last, when your bodies lie still and dead, whether it be in a palace or a poor man's hut, on a solitary Karroo plain or in a crowded city, whether you have been rich and famous or poor and unknown—what matters is this, that, if one should stand beside you and look down at you knowing all the story of your life, they should be able to say, 'This strong man's hand was always stretched out to cover those feebler; this great man's body never sought good or pleasure for itself at the price of something weaker.' Then, though no eye could see it, you would lie there, crowned—the noblest thing on earth, the body of a dead man who had lived the life of a man! No strength and no size and no beauty of body can ever give you that."   419–420

Is it not . . . because no individual is an isolated nomad? He may be one minute growth of the life of his race, of humanity, of living things on earth. Is an artist not simply a man in whom some of the accumulated life of his race, of the millions of human creatures who have been his ancestors in the ages past, is stored? Is not much of his work, if it be true artistic work, like the work of the bee who makes her perfect polygonal cell in the first year of her life? Is not the curious confidence of the artist that he is right due to the fact that he is working by a curious inborn necessity? You argue with the bee in vain, a four-sided cell is better; she builds it six; and, if you ask her why, she says she must—it is so, that's all! Her whole cell is meaningless unless you realize the storing of the honey and the bees that have yet to be born whom she has never seen and who will feed on the honey—but she builds.   450

"Yes," she said . . . "but, isn't the answer something the same? The life and movement in a single finger is quite incomprehensible unless you know that it belongs to a hand and acts as part of it, and a whole hand with all its functions and movements is quite incomprehensible unless you know it as part of a complex body with a life bound to it. We know the man, and we know a little the race and the life on earth which that expresses; but the life of which is it only part—of that we know nothing; and that is the moving power."

   "Oh yes," he said, "the life of which we know nothing—that is it!"

"I wish they gave it a larger name," she said.

"Yes," he said, "the name circumscribes it." 451

I can fancy that, if a man were shut for years in some lonely castle by a lake, with no human companion and no hope of escape, he yet might find life tolerable if he found in his prison an old block and carved it year after year; and that, when the time came for him to be led out to execution, rather than that his captor should see it, rather than that they should possess it who could not understand it, he might take out his knife and utterly destroy it; but I have fancied also how he would have clambered up and dropped it out of the small window into the lake below, in the hope, as they led him to death, that some day it might be found and might fall into the hands of one who would understand it, and that all the agony and all the hope and despair graven into the block in those long years would find an answer in another heart. They would never know who had carved it, but the thing would live in another soul; and so I have fancied death would be easier to him. I think no artist need fear to give his work to the world because there are none who can understand. No human soul is so lonely as it feels itself, because no man is merely an individual but is a part of the great body of life; the thoughts he thinks are part of humanity's thoughts, the visions he sees are part of humanity's visions; the artist is only an eye in the great human body, seeing for those who share his life: somewhere, some time, his own exist. 456

I have sometimes thought . . . it would be a terrible thing if, when death came to a man or woman, there stood about his bed, reproaching him, not for his sins, not for his crimes of commission and omission toward his fellow-men, but for the thoughts and the visions that had come to him, and which he, not for the sake of sensuous pleasure or gain, had thrust always into the background, saying, "Because of my art, my love and my relations to my fellow-men shall never suffer; there shall be no loaf of bread less baked, no sick left untended, no present human creature's need of me left unsatisfied because of it." And then, when he is dying, they gather round him, the things he might have incarnated and given life to—and would not. All that might have lived, and now must never live for ever, look at him with their large reproachful eyes—his own dead visions reproaching him; as the children a woman has aborted and refused to give life to might gather about her at last, saying, "We came to you; you, only you, could have given us life. Now we are dead forever. Was it worth it? All the sense of duty you satisfied, the sense of necessity you labored under: should you not have violated it and given us birth?" It has come upon me so vividly sometimes . . . that I have almost leaped out of bed to gain air—that suffocating sense that all his life long a man or a woman might live striving to do their duty and then at the end find it all wrong.   458–459

I see that, . . . but life is so terribly difficult. Men say it is so hard to do the right. I have never found that. The moment one knows what is right, I do it; it is easy to do it; the difficulty is to find what *is* right! There are such absolutely conflicting ideals; the ideal of absolute submission and endurance of wrong towards oneself— the ideal of noble resistance to all injustice and wrong, even when done to oneself—the ideal of the absolute devotion to the smaller, always present, call of life—and the ideal of a devotion to the larger aims sweeping all before it—all are beautiful. The agony of life is not the choice between good and evil, but between two evils or two goods!   459